THE NOAH PLAN®

MATHEMATICS CURRICULUM GUIDE

THE PRINCIPLE APPROACH®

KINDERGARTEN THROUGH TWELFTH GRADE

Arthur Paul Ricciardi

I must study politics and war that my sons may have liberty to study mathematics and philosophy. My sons ought to study mathematics and philosophy, geography, natural history, naval architecture, navigation, commerce and agriculture in order to give their children a right to study painting, poetry, music, architecture, statuary, tapestry, and porcelain.

(John Adams, Letter to Abigail, 1780)

FOUNDATION FOR AMERICAN CHRISTIAN EDUCATION

CHESAPEAKE, VIRGINIA

THE NOAH PLAN®
MATHEMATICS CURRICULUM GUIDE

THE PRINCIPLE APPROACH®

KINDERGARTEN THROUGH TWELFTH GRADE

Arthur Paul Ricciardi

Edited by Elizabeth L. Youmans

SECOND EDITION
MARCH 2005

ISBN 0-912498-39-0

Graphic Design and Layout,
Desta Garrett

Copyediting,
Sarah Huston

All Scripture references are taken from either the King James Version or
the New International Version of the Bible unless otherwise noted.

Cover Painting
Raphael, *The School of Athens* detail, 1510–11,
Fresco Vatican, Stanza della Segnatura, Rome

The cover art is a detail taken from Raphael's magnificant fresco, *The School of Athens*, painted in the Vatican's Stanza della Segnatura in 1510. The fresco's themes are mathematics, number, ratio, and harmony.

The detail is of Euclid, the father of deductive reasoning. No work, except the Bible, has been more widely used, edited, or studied or has exercised a greater influence on scientific thinking than Euclid's *Elements*.

The Foundation for
American Christian Education
P.O. BOX 9588, CHESAPEAKE, VIRGINIA 23321

Ordering and catalogue
800-352-3223 • www.face.net

ACKNOWLEDGMENTS

This Mathematics Curriculum Guide exists because of the providence of God. As I restructured *The Noah Plan*® math curriculum, I learned much about mathematics. As I developed and wrote this guide, I learned even more about God and His faithfulness. He provided the desire, resources, time, energy, and ability for me to write. It is a testimony to the love and grace of the living God for His servants that He provided me with a mathematical education by direct deposition.

> Beautiful Savior! Lord of the nations!
> Son of God and Son of man! Glory and honor,
> Praise, adoration, now and forevermore be Thine!
> (Words by Muenster Gesangbuch, translated by Joseph A. Seiss)

I especially acknowledge the continuous support of my loving, dedicated, and loyal wife of thirty-five years, Rosemarie, a Principle Approach® master teacher in her own right. It was her unceasing prayer and patience that enabled me to complete the original volume and this second edition.

My thanks are extended to the faculty of StoneBridge School, who prayed for me and implemented the teaching philosophy and methods which imparted life, validity, and demonstration to the curriculum. A special note of appreciation is extended to StoneBridge teachers Sheree Beale, Susan Cognion, Cheryl Hunnewell, and Hut Lindner. I also appreciate the many StoneBridge students who encouraged me in this project, especially my seventh-grade homeroom classes, as well as third grader Ricky Schroff and sixth grader Renee Doussard.

Additionally, my sincerest and warmest gratitude is extended to Dr. Elizabeth Youmans for her guidance and encouragement and her tireless inspiration and editing efforts during the initial project.

My appreciation is extended to Miss Rosalie Slater, cofounder and president of the Foundation for American Christian Education, and Dr. Carole Adams, its executive vice president, for entrusting this project to me.

Finally, sincere gratitude is extended to the many Principle Approach teachers around the nation—Roy and Sandy McKasson, Ruth Smith, James Rose, James and Barbara Kilkenny, and Katherine Dang—for planting the seeds of the Principle Approach in my heart in the early 1980s.

This Mathematics Curriculum Guide was greatly enhanced by two math educators: Drs. Joseph Ray and Joan Cotter. Dr. Ray, a math professor and curriculum writer, was a contemporary of Abraham Lincoln, a time when youth read their schoolbooks and then committed time to reading their Bibles, singing hymns, and enjoying Greek and Roman classics in their original languages. Ray delighted his students by joining them in sports and used these opportunities successfully to teach abstract concepts of mathematics to them. For the next fifty years, most Americans were challenged to excellence in math with *Ray's*™ *Arithmetics*. Secondly, God providentially inspired and equipped Dr. Cotter to create and publish *RightStart*™, an American abacus-based nontraditional approach to teaching and learning mathematics. Cotter's wholistic, practical, and friendly approach appeals to young children, who are able to learn the principles of mathematics through this curriculum. An engineer who designed her own abacus for use in her curriculum, she has spent time in the Foundation demonstration school, instructed and inspired the primary school faculty, and imparted her love and ability to teach abstract math concepts to the school family. I am most appreciative.

I chose these curricula for *The Noah Plan* elementary math program to restore the study of the principles of mathematics and their practical applications to American Christian curriculum. My hope is that the children in this rising generation will come to love mathematics and see in this discipline the nature and character of the living God, who spoke into existence the creation of the universe through the language of mathematics. May His people once again hear His voice in mathematics and draw all children to Christ for His Story.

Arthur Paul Ricciardi, Ed.D.
Chesapeake, Virginia
October, 2004

FOREWORD

This guide is presented in response to the challenge facing American Christian teachers and parents to fully train and equip the next generation for Christian life and leadership in the twenty-first century. In an age now driven by the relentless necessity of scientific and technological advances, the preparation our students receive in mathematics is critical for their role in fulfilling God's cultural mandate.

In the twenty-first century, the National Commission on Math and Science Teaching, headed by former astronaut John Glenn, studied why, as American children get older, they consistently do more poorly than other nations' children on math and science tests. The conclusion of the Commission in September, 2000 was that America's math and science teachers are not adequately trained. More than twenty-five percent of high school math and science teachers lack even a college minor in those areas. Their solution was to spend billions of tax-payer dollars to train math and science teachers![1]

For those teachers who *have* mastered the disciplines of mathematics, many do not apply mathematics to the sciences or the everyday world around them. In *Mathematics: Is God Silent?*, the author noted that "roughly five percent of high school math teachers have any idea of how mathematics is used in science. Most haven't any notion of why anyone wants mathematics."[2] Because humanistic presuppositions taught in America's university math courses deny the existence of a Biblical Creator God, many teachers see mathematics as just a mental construct or an intellectual game. For those elementary teachers who have always been afraid and mystified by the advanced branches of mathematics, many have imparted this same self-defeating spirit to their students.

This report should concern American Christian educators who, for the most part, have looked to progressive educators for their math curriculum in the twentieth century Christian school movement. The pendulum has swung from traditional math to New Math and now to new New Math resulting in a "math war" at the end of the century and lower math scores for American students in comparison to the students of other industrialized nations of the world. Until recently, the primary goal of America's math curriculum has been to teach children a core content associated with foundational math knowledge through direct teaching. Now even this most basic educational goal has been abandoned. How long will it be before this "feel-good math" approach finds its way into the Christian classroom?

The solution for America's crisis in math education is not to spend additional billions of dollars in a newly crafted math training program, but to replace the prevailing secular, eclectic philosophy of education with the Biblical, Christian philosophy of education and scholarship that was so prevalent in the founding and constitutional generations.

There are basically three approaches Christian educators take when selecting and teaching a mathematics curriculum:

1) Math is seen as a "secular" subject and the curriculum is chosen and taught much as it is in the public school system. Students are not introduced to God as the Author of mathematics and, therefore, are never challenged to see how math connects to the unity of all knowledge;
2) Secular math curricula are "Christianized" by lacquering textbook pages with Scripture verses. Students and parents are misled into believing that a Biblical view of mathematics is being imparted;
3) The Word of God and its principles are the solid rock foundation for developing and teaching mathematics. Students are inspired to see the attributes of God's nature and character and to comprehend His divine purposes for math. God's governing principles, as well as the principles of the subject, are taught as truth. God is honored as the Author of mathematics and His Spirit inspires both teacher and student to think with the mind of Christ in mathematics. "But there is a spirit in man: and the inspiration of the Almighty giveth them understanding." (Job 32:8)

This Biblical approach to teaching and learning is called the Principle Approach®. It is "America's historic method of reasoning which places the Truths of God's Word at the heart of every subject."[3] Each subject in the curriculum is developed through the unifying, core principles of God's Word and a precisely defined vocabulary. Its reflective Notebook Method teaches children to think and reason in the subject with the

1 "American Schools Lacking," September 27, 2000, www.ABCnews.com.

2 James Nickel, *Mathematics: Is God Silent?* Vallecito, CA: Ross House Books, 1990, 109.

3 Rosalie J. Slater, *Teaching and Learning America's Christian History: The Principle Approach.* San Francisco: Foundation for American Christian Education, 1965, 52.

revelation of Scripture, both Biblically and governmentally, and equips them with a Biblical, Christian world- and life view for a lifetime of liberty in learning and problem solving.

The Noah Plan® Mathematics Curriculum Guide employs the Principle Approach® in conjunction with published curricular programs and advanced math textbooks. It begins with a new, American abacus-based, non-traditional curriculum for primary grades (K–4), which teaches and demonstrates the principles of the art of computation. A nineteenth century, highly-proven, middle school (5–7) curriculum, that emphasizes thinking mathematically and problem solving with applications to the worlds of business and finance, leads students toward mastery of the advanced branches (8–12) of mathematics beginning with Algebra 1 in the eighth grade and concluding with calculus. Each course of study begins by laying the Biblical foundation of mathematics and emphasizes both the Biblical principles and those of the individual branch of mathematics being studied.

That which has been lost to American Christian mathematics education is now restored—the wonder and knowledge that mathematics is a language, the language expressed in God's creation. In the beginning God spoke, and by the word of His power (Hebrews 1:3) the heavens and the earth came into existence and are upheld. The patterns of God's speech laid the structure of the universe and describe for us the laws of His handiwork. Mathematics must once again be studied in the context of God's creation and be applied as the essential instrument of science. It is the foundation of all technical and scientific logic. When His principles, both Biblical and governmental, are applied to thinking and communicating mathematically, our students are prepared to wisely handle the sciences and technology of the twenty-first century for the higher purposes of God in Christ, His Story.

Elizabeth L. Youmans, Ed.D.
Editor

KEY

Abbreviations

The following are abbreviations used throughout this Guide for books published by the Foundation for American Christian Education (the Foundation):

B & C	*The Bible and the Constitution of the United States of America.* Verna M. Hall and Rosalie J. Slater.
C & P	*The Christian History of the American Revolution: Consider and Ponder.* Compiled by Verna M. Hall.
CHOC I	*The Christian History of the Constitution of the United States of America,* Vol. I: *Christian Self-Government.* Compiled by Verna M. Hall.
CHOC II	*The Christian History of the Constitution of the United States of America,* Vol. II: *Christian Self-Government with Union.* Compiled by Verna M. Hall.
NPMG	*The Noah Plan® Mathematics Curriculum Guide,* Arthur Paul Ricciardi
NPSDS	*The Noah Plan Self-Directed Study in the Principle Approach®.* Carole G. Adams and Elizabeth Youmans.
Rudiments	*Rudiments of America's Christian History and Government: Student Handbook.* Rosalie J. Slater and Verna M. Hall.
T & L	*Teaching and Learning America's Christian History: The Principle Approach.* Rosalie J. Slater,
Webster's 1828 *Dictionary*	*An American Dictionary of the English Language.* Noah Webster. Facsimile 1828 edition.

Trademarked and Registered Resources

Activities for Learning™	The Principle Approach
AL™ Abacus	*Ray's™ New Practical Arithmetic*
The Chain of Christianity®	*Ray's™ New Higher Arithmetic*
The Noah Plan	*RightStart™*

Principle Approach Model of Education

This diagram shows the components of the Principle Approach model of education—a philosophy, methodology, and curriculum that produce particular results and are governed by the Spirit of Christ.

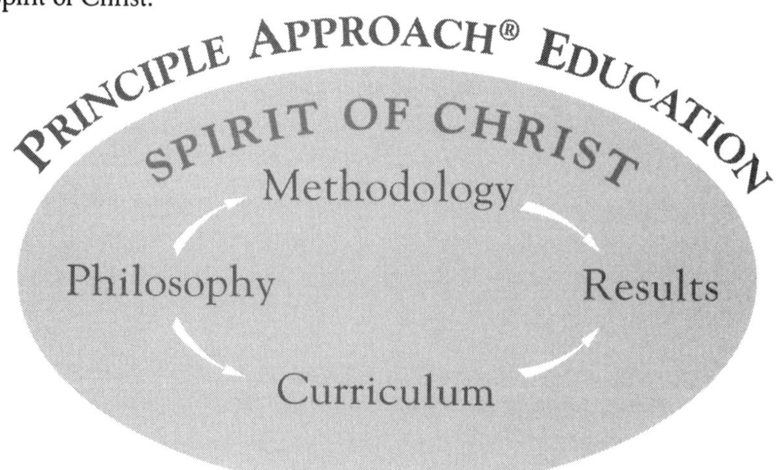

MATHEMATICS GUIDE OVERVIEW

The Noah Plan® Mathematics Curriculum Guide employs the Principle Approach® in teaching and learning mathematics. As defined by its architect, Rosalie J. Slater, "the Principle Approach is America's historic philosophy and reflective methodology that places the Truths of God's Word at the heart of all sound knowledge and learning." The Word is alive, active, God-breathed! The foundation and meaning of mathematics are revealed in the Bible—the source of wisdom that inspired Kepler, Galileo, Newton, and Bowditch.

Teaching and learning mathematics from a Biblical, principled approach produces lively math scholars who have the mental disposition to see God's excellent nature and character expressed in mathematics. God is the source of life, vigor, and cheerfulness for the study of mathematics. This life-source restores meaning and purpose to the study of mathematics, the language of creation. Teaching and learning mathematics from this philosophy require Christian methodology. No longer will the teacher be satisfied to teach bone-dry facts and boring rules to children, who are unreceptive to such methods. Instead, he will infuse life and a love for learning mathematics into the hearts and minds of students by demonstrating the great works of the Lord that govern all of creation.

This guide is divided into four sections:

1. The first chapter overviews the basic principles of mathematics in the Principle Approach with the practical curriculum charts that outline what to teach. The curriculum is applicable in any classroom or homeschool setting and demonstrates Biblical and mathematical principles essential for students to master the subject and apply the dominion mandate (Genesis 1:27–28). This kindergarten through twelfth grade curriculum enlivens the understanding of God's purposes and principles in mathematics and their applications to the sciences and technology.

2. The second chapter lays the Biblical and governmental foundations for teaching and learning mathematics. It defines a Biblical philosophy of mathematics and answers the question, "How do I teach mathematics in the Principle Approach?" It includes a Christian History Timeline of Mathematics with individuals God has used throughout time for Christ, His Story through math.

3. The third chapter provides Christian methods that instruct teachers how to develop a Biblical mathematics curriculum and how to teach students to reason governmentally and think mathematically. These methods reflect the nature and character of Christ, rather than the progressive character of modern education in mathematics. They emanate from a true Biblical, Christian philosophy of education and government and produce distinctively Christian results in mathematics students.

4. The appendix provides a variety of resources for teaching and learning mathematics, glossaries, and sample student notebook pages.

TABLE OF CONTENTS

The Whole Principle Approach® Curriculum

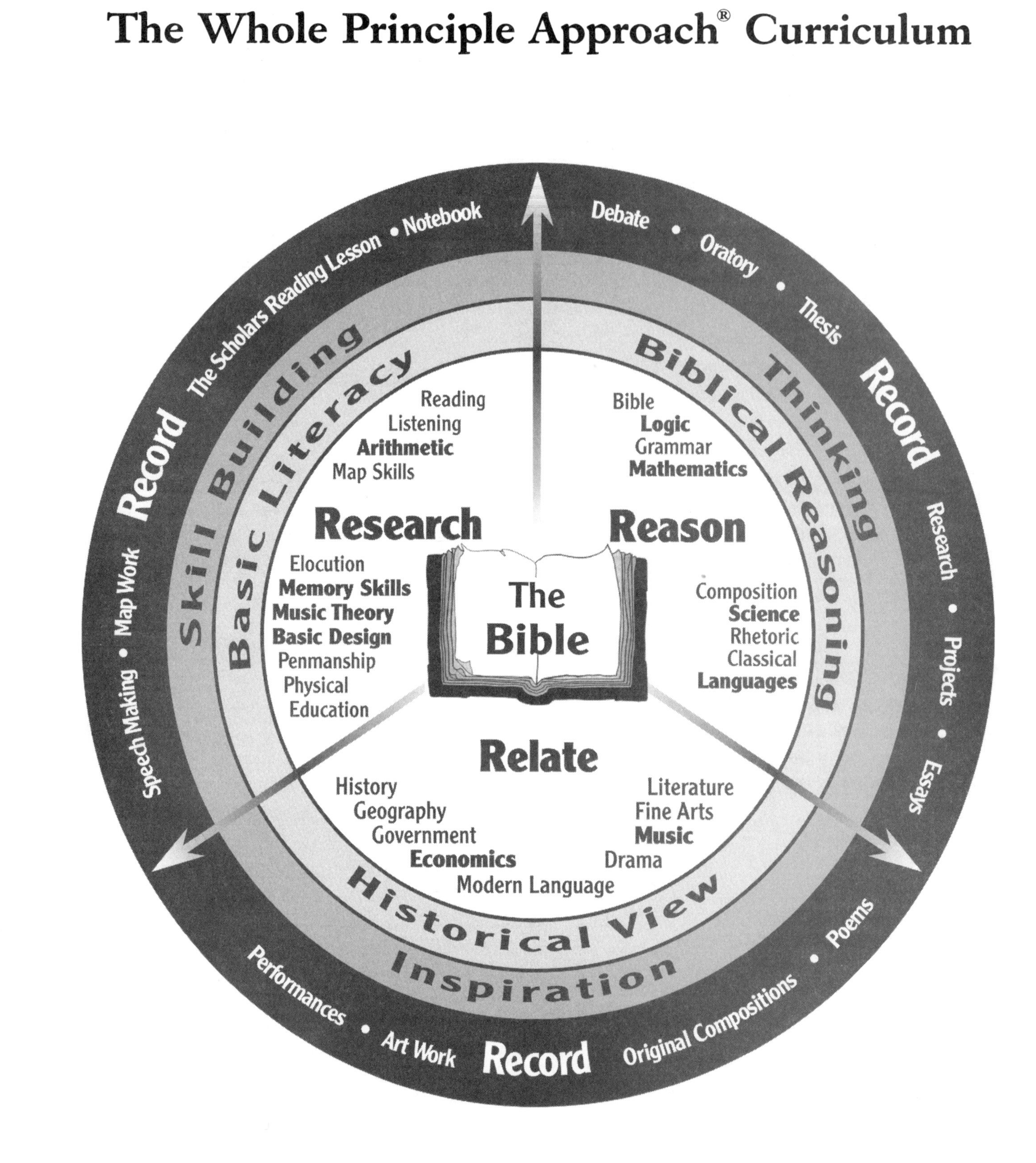

Cultivating Reasoning through the Grades

Grade Level	Metaphor	Research	Reason	Relate	Record
Kindergarten	Planting the seeds of all knowledge	Identifying the subjects by their principles being demonstrated	Understanding symbols (Examples: numerals, +, −, ×, ÷, =)	Oral language; mimicry; word problems; showing; demonstrating principles	Recognizing the notebook as a tool of learning
Primary School	Tending the seedlings (sunning; weeding; watering; regulating; fertilizing; guarding; cultivating)	Mastering the art of computation and the vocabulary of mathematics	Understanding internal to external; concrete thinking; using manipulatives; skill building	Recitation; rote; expository (writing); guided projects	The notebook as a tool of scholarship—notebook skills practiced and guided by teacher
Middle School	Growing the plant (pruning; guiding; correcting; transplanting; maturing; seasoning; making hardy)	Defining the principles of mathematics, the science of numbers	Understanding cause to effect; questioning; logic; critical thinking; scientific method	Independent projects (science)	Notebook mastery—a tool for lifelong independent learning
High School	Reaping the fruit (cycling growth and harvesting the fruit)!	Expressing and applying the principles of mathematics in life and learning	Original thinking and actual reasoning from a Biblical worldview	Apprenticeship (field of math or science); original science project	Habit and spirit of organized learning and Biblical scholarship inculcated

Chapter One
An American Christian Mathematics Curriculum

And He gave some as apostles, and some as prophets, and some as evangelists, and some as pastors and teachers, for the equipping of the saints for the work of service, to the building up of the body of Christ; until we all attain to the unity of the faith, and of the knowledge of the Son of God, to a mature man, to the measure of the stature which belongs to the fulness of Christ. As a result, we are no longer to be children, tossed here and there by waves, and carried about by every wind of doctrine, by the trickery of men, by craftiness in deceitful scheming; but speaking the truth in love, we are to grow up in all aspects into Him who is the head, even Christ, . . . [Therefore,] walk no longer just as the Gentiles also walk, in the futility of their mind, being darkened in their understanding, excluded from the life of God because of the . . . hardness of their heart; . . . [Y]ou did not learn Christ in this way, if indeed you have heard Him and have been taught in Him, just as truth is in Jesus, . . . that you be renewed in the spirit of your mind.

(Ephesians 4:11–23, NASB)

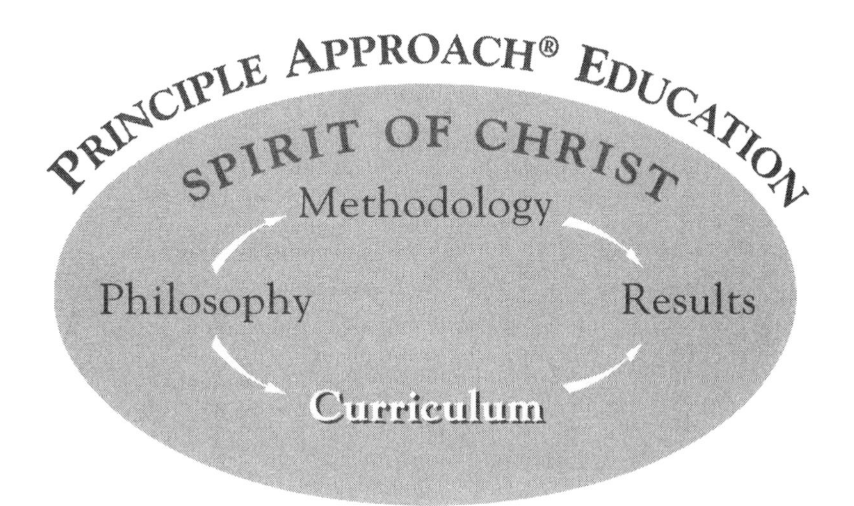

Notes

Introducing an American Christian Mathematics Curriculum

Well-taught, math is a thing of beauty, exciting in its logic, elegance, and coherence. Math is also a vital component of a good education. In part, the study of math is the study of problems and solutions. It builds both the analytic spirit and the deductive capacity on which intelligent thought depends. And it teaches students the value of precise thinking.

(William J. Bennett, 1987)

Throughout the ancient civilizations of the Middle East, Greece, and Rome, rudimentary mathematics was part of the basic education of a child. No discipline was held in more esteem than mathematics for the ancient classical Greeks, whose word *mathematica* means "to learn." The ancient Greek philosophers were skilled in mathematics. Euclid of Alexandria, the father of deductive reasoning, understood the value of logical thinking and promoted this essential method for determining the validity of an idea. His treatise on geometry in 300 B.C. entitled *The Elements* has been more widely used, edited, and studied and has exercised a greater influence on scientific thinking than any book except the Bible. As Western civilization progressed and Christianity pushed westward, the Middle Ages birthed the university system as a learning center and a classical liberal arts curriculum known as the *trivium* and *quadrivium*. Scholars adapted Greek education to their culture and taught arithmetic, geometry, music, and astronomy and the medieval church taught mathematics as training for theological reasoning.

In the grace and providence of God for Christ, His Story, the Bible was translated into the languages of the Europeans and birthed the Protestant Reformation in the 1500s. When the Bible came into the hands of the individual (not just the monks and priests, but the laity) the common man was now able to have his own copy of the Scriptures. The individual was soon able to reason with the revelation of God's Word for himself. His mind was renewed and his reasoning was set free from the bondage of false philosophies and doctrines and the dependence upon others to interpret the meaning of life. God and His Word attained pre-eminence as philosophers and mathematicians studied and reflected upon His nature and character in mathematics and the sciences.

Trained to reason with Biblical principles in every academic discipline and sphere of life, the European reformers placed a high value on education, and Biblical scholarship laid the foundation for American Christian government and education. The Bible became their first book of instruction, both for early childhood and college education, as well as their political textbook for reasoning into the civil realm and its institutions. Parents took seriously their divine role to train up their children in the admonition of the Lord and used the Bible to teach reading and vocabulary, reasoning and writing skills. Mathematics was known as the language of the sciences. Johannes Kepler, renowned sixteenth century mathematician and scientist, wrote, "The chief aim of all investigations of the external world should be to discover the rational order and harmony which has been imposed on it by God and which He revealed to us in the language of mathematics." (Johannes Kepler, *Defundamentis Astrologiae Certioribus:* Thesis XX, 1601.)

The chief aim of all investigations of the external world should be to discover the rational order and harmony which has been imposed on it by God and which He revealed to us in the language of mathematics.
(Johannes Kepler)

Notes

The Standard for American Christian Scholarship

Colonial American educators set the standard of Christian scholarship through their use of the Bible, their first book of instruction and reasoning. Sixteen years after the Pilgrims landed in the New World, Harvard College was founded in the New England wilderness to train ministers of the Gospel. In 1636 the primary educators of the day were the clergy, whose mission it was to equip their progeny. Europe's classical education was filtered through the reformers' distinctly Christian worldview, and the living principles of the Bible governed reasoning for America's forefathers in the home, the church, and the civil realm giving life and structure to their convictions, family life, laws, institutions, and founding documents. Young children were taught to read and cipher, and those who attended Latin schools for college entrance were rigorously trained in the higher branches of mathematics to cultivate the intellect by developing critical habits of the mind in logical and abstract thinking.

Forefather John Adams wrote in his diary that mathematics "proved the extent of the human mind to be more spacious and capable than any other science." His first son, John Quincy, was home and self-educated prior to traveling with his father in Europe and being assigned at the age of fourteen to Russia as the Diplomatic Secretary to Francis Dana in 1781! In 1785 father John Adams wrote a letter to Professor Waterhouse at Harvard College to seek admission for his son. Knowing that Harvard required a difficult entrance examination, he felt obliged to apologize for young John Quincy's "smatterings" in the study of math:

> In mathematics I hope he will pass muster. In the course of the last year, instead of playing cards like the fashionable world, I have spent my evenings with him. We went with some accuracy through the geometry in the Preceptor, the eight books of Simpson's Euclid in Latin, and compared it, problem by problem and theorem by theorem, with le père de Chales in French; we went through plane trigonometry and plain sailing, Fenning's Algebra, and the decimal fractions, arithmetical and geometrical proportions, and the conic sections in Ward's mathematics. I then attempted a sublime flight, and endeavored to give him some idea of the differential method of calculation of the Marquis de L'Hopital, and the method of fluxions and infinite series of Sir Isaac Newton; but alas! it is thirty years since I thought of mathematics, and I found I had lost the little I once knew, especially of these higher branches of geometry, so that he is yet but a smatterer, like his father. However, he has a foundation laid, which will enable him with a year's attendance on the mathematical professor, to make the necessary proficiency for a degree.[1]

John Quincy was admitted as a junior to Harvard College and graduated second in his class. A lifelong student of God's Word, he served the nation for over fifty years as a Christian statesman and sixth president. (Oh, that the twenty-first century American high school student would be so well prepared!)

From the 1750s to 1900, mathematics was taught with a comprehensive approach in the United States that systematically began with simple arithmetic problems to build within the citizenry the ability to reason with basic mathematical ideas. The methodology emphasized mental and oral arithmetic that preceded written arithmetic, as a means of assuring the teacher and the student that understanding of the subject had been achieved. It encompassed more than just knowing how to add a series of numbers on paper. Principles of computation, knowledge, and reasoning had to be applied in order to solve a problem. This ability to apply principles, rules, and the language of mathematics to solve problems produced within the learner faith, self-reliance, and confidence—the academically independent learner. These traits contributed to building a Christian work ethic and a faithful and overcoming character in the learner.

---

1 Rosalie J. Slater, "The Education of John Quincy Adams: The Character for a Christian Republic" in Verna Hall's *The Christian History of the American Revolution: Consider and Ponder.* San Francisco: Foundation for American Christian Education, 1988, 611.

Notes

Twentieth Century Mathematics Education

In the twentieth century, math education shifted from a God-centered philosophy to a humanistic philosophy. Like every other subject in the American curriculum, the pendulum of math curriculum and methodology has swung back and forth between direct instruction, which requires a master teacher, a textbook, and instruction and drill (based upon the knowledge and methods gleaned over the centuries), to the "new New Math," which asks students to figure things out for themselves and construct their own meanings and understandings. The effect of shifting from a curriculum and methodology that are strong in knowing math facts, building mental and oral math competency, and requiring drill and practice, to one requiring trial and error investigations, intuitive insights, and applications to real life has been dramatically disappointing.

The Third International Mathematics and Science Study released in 1998 provided alarming statistics for United States math education. It was conducted to gauge how close the United States was to the goal of being first in the world in mathematics and science achievement. They tested students from 41 industrialized countries in the fourth, eighth, and twelfth grades for math ability. While the U.S. fourth graders did well compared to children of other countries and eighth graders ranked near the middle, twelfth grade students from the United States ranked a dismal 38th, out-scoring their peers in just three countries—Lithuania, Cypress, and South Africa. More unnerving than the seniors' performance, however, is the realization that "the United States appears to be the only country in the world where children seem to do [relatively] worse in math the older they get and the more time they spend in school."[2] Data from national sources are just as alarming. The National Assessment of Educational Progress determined that only one out of five (20%) fourth graders and only one out of four (25%) eighth graders was proficient in math in 1996.

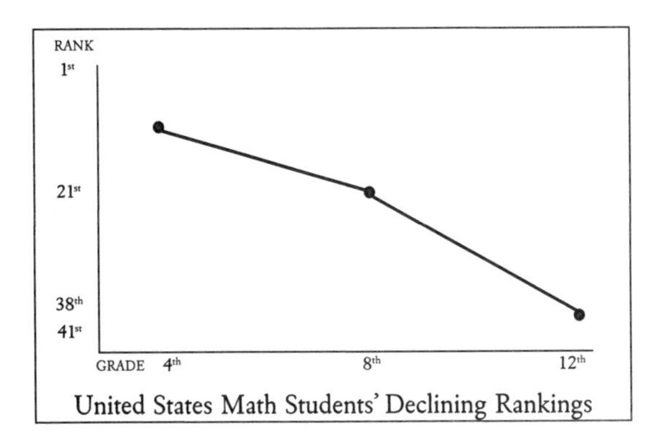

United States Math Students' Declining Rankings

In his book published in 1999 entitled *The Educated Child,* William J. Bennett cited many causes of the decline in math proficiency:

- Disorganized curriculum structure
- Inadequately trained teachers
- Lack of clear, tough academic standards
- Basic arithmetic not taught at the primary level
- "Dumbed down" textbooks and lesson plans
- Practice and applying effort to learn fundamentals not required of students

There has also been a dramatic decline in the College Board SAT mathematics scores. Is the shift from mental mathematics, which assures the understanding of its branches, a factor in this national decline? At the turn of the century, the primary-aged student of arithmetic was actively led through daily mental and oral practice. There was a minimum of writing and a maximum of thinking. This approach trained minds to *do* and to *apply* mathematics independently of pencil and paper. During that era, educators recognized the limitations of the learner, yet they realized that mathematical principles are demonstrable. Therefore, they taught beginners by:

- Demonstrating the principles of mathematics
- Employing the vocabulary of the subject
- Depending upon and requiring mental effort, not talent
- Using few manipulative tools
- Introducing abstract symbols and signs to the learner

This approach developed the strong foundation in mathematics that served the learner dependably in his station for an entire lifetime.

---

2 William Bennett, Chester Finn, and John Cribb, *The Educated Child.* New York: The Free Press, 1999, 283.

Notes

An American Christian Approach for the Twenty-First Century: The Principle Approach®

Mathematics is a language and a precisely structured discipline; therefore, teaching it should reflect a precise structure and methodology. The Principle Approach offers the Christian teacher and homeschooling parent the opportunity to inspirit and structure mathematics education through the following distinctives:

1. Laying a Biblical foundation for the subject, glorifying God as the author, and giving preeminence for the authority of His Word within the subject.

2. Placing the subject on the Chain of Christianity® moving westward, teaching God's Gospel purposes for the subject, and forming individual character in the lives of men and nations.

3. Teaching the art of learning for subject mastery by Biblical principles and leading ideas, emphasizing thinking and deductive reasoning with truth, rather than pursuing and memorizing information.

4. Arranging the teaching of the subject whole to its parts, and connecting it to the complete body of knowledge in a unity of truth.

5. Developing subject overviews to create a whole approach unified by principles and structure.

6. Building understanding through the use of a precise vocabulary, holding students responsible for word definitions, and daily writing in every subject.

7. Employing the Notebook Method as the tool of scholarship for developing the curriculum, cultivating the mind and character of Christ, and producing a permanent record of learning through the 4-R's:

   Research:
   - Lay the foundation of teaching and learning the knowledge of God in all the branches of mathematics on the Truths of God's Word —the Biblical principles that govern the subject and provide the structure for study
   - Define the vocabulary of the subject
   - Identify the mathematical principles of each branch of mathematics

   Reason:
   - Restore sound habits for cultivating the Christian mind, such as: thinking logically and reasoning deductively with principles; scrutinizing problems; breaking large problems into smaller parts
   - Choose the best approach for problem solving
   - Require "correct" answers by calculating with exactness

   Relate:
   - Apply mathematical principles to technology and the sciences
   - Apply lessons learned from Christian history of mathematics and mathematicians
   - Form Christian character and a Christian work ethic
   - Tutor others

   Record:
   - Express answers clearly in mathematical notation
   - Maintain a permanent record of study

8. Planting all the seeds of knowledge for each subject in kindergarten, and building understanding through the years line upon line, precept upon precept.

Notes

Foundational Principles that Undergird *The Noah Plan*® Mathematics Curriculum

1. Teaching and learning mathematics begins with the Living God and the authority of His Word, the Bible. Creator God is the source of all knowledge and wisdom. His Word is truth and is foundational and authoritative in all disciplines of study. His principles and laws are immutable. When mathematics is taught in light of Biblical truth, students' hearts and minds are inspired to see the attributes of God's nature and character, as well as His eternal principles of truth.

   "Thy word is true from the beginning: and every one of thy righteous judgments endureth for ever." (Psalm 119:160)

   "Sanctify them through thy truth: thy word is truth." (John 17:17)

   "For since the creation of the world His invisible attributes, His eternal power and divine nature, have been clearly seen, being understood through what has been made, so that they are without excuse." (Romans 1:20, NASB)

   "See to it that no one takes you captive through philosophy and empty deception, according to the tradition of men, according to the elementary principles of the world, rather than according to Christ." (Colossians 2:8, NASB)

2. All subjects form a unity of truth when taught from a Biblical, Christian perspective. "All knowledge forms one whole, because its subject matter is one; for the universe in its length and breadth is so intimately knit together that we cannot separate off portion from portion, and operation from operation except by mental abstraction."[1] Mastering the disciplines of mathematics and their applications to problem solving are foundational for a well-rounded education and for acquiring a Biblical, Christian world- and life view.

   "He is the image of the invisible God, the firstborn of all creation. For by Him all things were created, both in the heavens and on earth, visible and invisible, whether thrones or dominions or rulers or authorities—all things have been created by Him and for Him. He is before all things, and in Him all things hold together." (Colossians 1:15–17, NASB)

3. Mathematics is not a secular subject. All truth is God's truth. There is no dichotomy between the sacred and the secular for the thinking Christian. Mathematics is the language of God revealed in creation, the patterns of which laid the structure of the universe and describe for man the laws of His handiwork. It is the foundation for all technical and scientific logic. Mathematics is the key to understanding the physical world and is taught in the context of science and technology. "The profound study of nature is the most fertile source of mathematical discoveries." (Joseph Fourier)

   "In the beginning God created the heavens and the earth. The earth was formless and void, and darkness was over the surface of the deep, and the Spirit of God was moving over the surface of the waters. Then God said, 'Let there be light'; and there was light." (Genesis 1:1–3, NASB)

   "The heavens declare the glory of God; And the firmament shows His handiwork. Day unto day utters speech, And night unto night reveals knowledge. There is no speech nor language Where their voice is not heard." (Psalm 19:1–3, NKJV)

4. Mathematics is a disciplined thought structure. Abstract thought has a concrete foundation. The coherence between abstract models and concrete reality, emphasizing both deductive and inductive thinking, is demonstrated in the primary grade-level curriculum and emphasized in higher level mathematics.

   "In the beginning was the Word, and the Word was with God, and the Word was God. He was

---

[1] John Henry Cardinal Newman, *The Scope and Nature of University Education*. New York: E. P. Dutton, 1958, 37.

Notes

in the beginning with God. All things came into being through Him, and apart from Him nothing came into being that has come into being. And the Word became flesh, and dwelt among us, and we saw His glory." (John 1:1–3, 14a, NASB)

"God, after He spoke long ago to the fathers in the prophets in many portions and in many ways, in these last days has spoken to us in His Son, whom He appointed heir of all things, through whom also He made the world. And He is the radiance of His glory and the exact representation of His nature, and upholds all things by the word of His power." (Hebrews 1:1–3a, NASB)

5. The mastery of mathematics as a discipline is essential if man is to fulfill the cultural mandate. Applications to technology, the sciences, and practical problem solving are emphasized throughout the mathematics curriculum so that students can integrate mathematical principles to all of life and learning.

"God created man in His own image, in the image of God He created him; male and female He created them. God blessed them; and God said to them, 'Be fruitful and multiply, and fill the earth, and subdue it; and rule over the fish of the sea and over the birds of the sky and over every living thing that moves on the earth.'" (Genesis 1:27–28, NASB)

6. The place of mathematics on the Chain of Christianity® is taught. Both the history and philosophy of the branches of math are studied in the light of Christ, His Story. Knowing God and His hand in history, as He divinely directs individuals and nations for His Gospel purposes, inspires the Christian math teacher to not only teach the mechanics of mathematics, but also the history of math and her mathematicians as they relate to the propagation of the Gospel and liberty for the individual and for nations.

"Make for yourself an ark of gopher wood; you shall make the ark with rooms, and shall cover it inside and out with pitch. This is how you shall make it: the length of the ark three hundred cubits, its breadth fifty cubits, and its height thirty cubits. You shall make a window for the ark, and finish it to a cubit from the top; and set the door of the ark in the side of it; you shall make it with lower, second, and third decks." (Genesis 6:14–16, NASB)

A mathematics curriculum that begins with God's principles and is taught by a skillful and inspired Christian mathematician will communicate the eternal purposes and principles of mathematics to the minds and hearts of students. With a rich and inspired curriculum, students are able to master mathematical knowledge and principles without meaningless and endless review of previously taught material. This view of curriculum frees teachers and students to delve deeply into mathematical ideas that reveal the majesty and excellence of the attributes of God's nature and character as they are seen in the physical creation.

An American abacus-based curriculum has been chosen for the primary grades (K–4). Developed in the 1990s, Dr. Joan Cotter's *RightStart*™ curriculum begins in the kindergarten program with concrete experiences and develops meaning and purpose for understanding math symbols. Language patterns and visualization of numbers in groupings through the use of the abacus are used to teach place value and representing quantities. Visualization strategies offer efficient techniques for learning math facts. Children progress from entering and rearranging quantities physically, to entering the quantities physically but rearranging them mentally, then to performing the entire process mentally. These components of learning help young children obtain mathematical knowledge that develops accurate computation skills and leads to an increase in abstract thinking.

A traditional problem-solving curriculum has been chosen for the middle school grades (5–7). Written in the 1860s, *Rays*™ *Arithmetics* center on the application of mathematical principles and logical thinking for solving a wide variety of useful and practical business problems and have proven effective over the century. Both curricula eliminate the rote-based mathematics approach that focuses on meaningless and endless review of previously taught materials and requires students to painfully study and memorize ideas and procedures year after year. Teachers are pressured to cover huge amounts of material at breakneck speeds causing

Notes

students to forget much of the material when using rote-based materials.

The textbooks for teaching the branches of mathematics (8–12)—algebra, geometry, trigonometry, and calculus—have been selected based upon the mastery of each discipline and its application to the sciences and technology.

The Noah Plan® Mathematics Curriculum produces students who are capable of reasoning Biblically and thinking mathematically, students able to solve complex mathematical problems and apply principles to life and learning. Prepared for college entrance or career choices, students are able to assume leadership in the home, church and civil spheres.

Working Definitions

mathematics:

1. [L. *mathematica,* from Gr. to learn] The science of quantity; the science which treats of magnitude and number, or of whatever can be measured or numbered. . . . It is the peculiar excellence of *mathematics,* that its principles are demonstrable. Arithmetic, geometry, algebra, trigonometry, and conic sections are branches of *mathematics.* (Webster's 1828 *Dictionary)*
2. Mathematics is the language of God expressed in creation, the patterns of which laid the structure of the universe and describe the laws of His handiwork. (Editor)
3. Mathematics describes the set of perpetual laws with which God made manifest and upholds the physical universe. It is the expression of His orderly nature that describes the quantative relationships governing the individual members of creation, from the micro- to the macro-cosmos (Hebrews 1:3; Colossians 1:17). (Editor)
4. An entity which perhaps always exists in the mind of God, and which is for man the universal expression of His creative and sustaining word of power. (Larry Zimmerman)[1]

curriculum: [L. *curriculum,* a running course, race, career.] A specific course of study or collectively all the courses of study in a school, university, etc.

course: (1) A methodical series, *applied to the arts or the sciences;* a systematized order of principles in arts or sciences, for illustration or instruction. (2) Manner of proceeding; way of life or conduct; . . . series of actions. (Webster's 1828 *Dictionary*)

mathematics curriculum: The whole body of knowledge taught (branches of mathematics); how it is ordered through the years (scope and sequence); and the manner (methods and tools) used for teaching it.

American Christian mathematics curriculum: Its philosophy is rooted in the Principle Approach®, America's historic and Biblical method of reasoning which places the Truths of God's Word at the heart of every subject. God's divine nature and character, as well as His Word, are laid as the solid rock foundation. An American Christian mathematics curriculum employs the Notebook Method (the 4-R's) for thinking mathematically and reasoning governmentally. The Notebook Method builds in each student the mind and character of Christ which are necessary to commission each graduate to enter the world of diverse challenges with Biblical solutions and to sustain our American Christian constitutional republic.

---

1 Larry Zimmerman, "Mathematics: Is God Silent? Part II," *The Biblical Educator,* Vol. II, No. 2. Sterling, VA: Institute for Christian Economics, 1980.

Notes

Reasons for Curricular Choices

It is the peculiar excellence of mathematics, that its principles are demonstrable.

(Noah Webster's 1828 *Dictionary*)

Reasons for choosing *RightStart*™ and *Ray's*™ *Arithmetics* are that they:

- Teach, demonstrate, and apply the principles that govern the subject, which glorifies God
- Begin with concrete experiences and move to the abstract
- Bring meaning and purpose to mathematical symbols
- Incorporate mathematical activities which develop understanding
- Provide useful applications to solve practical problems
- Cause the learner to think mathematically
- Reduce the amount of drill because idea is understood
- Use rich vocabulary of the subject
- Require effort not talent
- Teach the language and vocabulary of mathematics
- Teach mathematics as a language using suffix flow charts
- Make consistent use of one good manipulative—the abacus
- Develop stewardship of time
- Teach all learning styles consistently
- Teach mental imaging of quantities rather than counting units
- Teach the art of computation developmentally
- Produce an excellent concept of quantity
- Apply mathematical concepts to the sciences, fine arts, technology, and business
- Teach whole-to-part; known to the unknown
- Are teacher- and student-friendly
- Develop mathematical concepts years earlier
- Teach using value-naming
- Teach using a base ten, sub-base five approach
- Uphold local value immediately and consistently
- Encourage independent learning and thinking
- View mathematics as a tool of thinking
- Inspire the love of mathematics
- Teach and require student to use higher-order thinking skills: problem solving, modeling, applying, proving, justifying, and communicating
- Teach student to mentally perform arithmetical processes with speed and accuracy
- Teach "line upon line, precept upon precept"
- Teach strategies for problem solving
- Spend more time on fewer problems of greater quality
- Teach early introduction to multi-digit addition and subtraction
- Teach in a classical, systematic, and principled style

Additionally, *Ray's*™ *Arithmetics*:

- Develop the science of numbers practically
- State the principles and rules clearly
- Present examples for principles and rules in order of increasing difficulty
- Provide teacher and student with mathematical challenges
- Demonstrate a practical character and logical exactness in mathematics
- Lead toward mastery of arithmetic by seventh grade
- Teach thinking through problem solving and logic in arithmetic
- Explain each principle clearly by analysis or solution of simple examples from which a rule is derived, reasoning cause to effect
- Serve as a lifetime reference books for the student

Branches of Mathematics Applied to Problem Solving

Branch	Definition	Applied to Problem Solving
Algebra	A generalization of arithmetic. Classical algebra is concerned with finding solutions to equations governed by the commutative, associative, and distributive laws.	Navigation; surveying; optics; lenses; projectile paths; volumes; roots; areas; engineering; architecture
Arithmetic	A branch of mathematics and part of algebra concerned with the fundamental operations of addition, subtraction, multiplication, and division of numbers as an art and a science.	Insurance; premium & discount; engineering; bookkeeping; accounting; stocks & bonds commission & brokerage; taxes; revenue; interest; partnership; averaging; series; progressions; architecture
Geometry	The branch of mathematics concerned with the properties of and relationships between points, lines, planes, figures, solids, and surfaces.	Euclidean geometry; non-Euclidean geometry; Cartesian coordinates; analytic geometry; algebraic geometry; descriptive geometry; differential geometry; projective geometry; architecture
Trigonometry and Conic Sections	The branch of mathematics in which the principles of geometry are applied to triangles and the sections of a cone.	Astronomy; navigation; surveying; physics; optics; engineering; architecture
Calculus	The branch of mathematics that studies continuously changing quantities.	Vector analysis; tensor analysis; statistics; probability; computer science; architecture

Components of the Whole Mathematics Curriculum

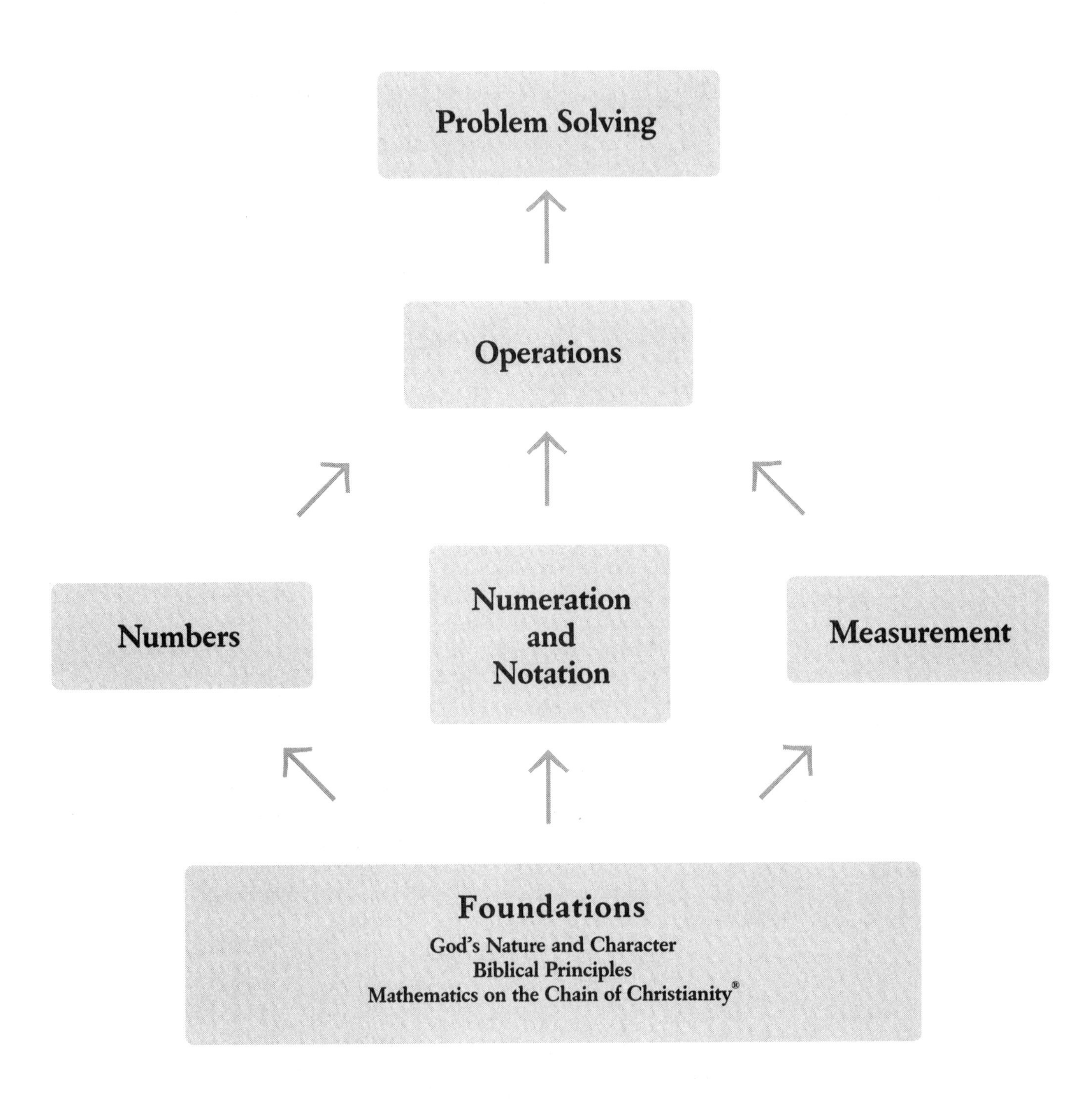

Notes

Key Definitions of the Mathematics Curriculum Components

1. **Foundations:**

foundation, *n.* The basis or ground-work . . . ; that on which any thing stands, and by which it is supported. A free government has its *foundation* in the choice and consent of the people to be governed. Christ is the *foundation* of the church. *Behold, I lay in Zion for a* foundation, *a stone—a precious corner-stone.* (Isaiah 28) *Other* foundation *can no man lay than that which is laid, which is Jesus Christ.* (1 Corinthians 3)
(Webster's 1828 *Dictionary*)

Foundations in the mathematics curriculum are God's nature and character, the Biblical principles which are found in God's Word, and the principles of the discipline being studied and math and mathematicians on the Chain of Christianity®.

This component provides the *why* of mathematics study and lays the foundation for mathematics in every grade securely upon principles that frame the study of all mathematics and underpin the development of mathematical skills.

2. **Numbers:**

number, *n.* [L. *numerus;* . . .] The designation of a unit in reference to other units, or in reckoning, counting, or enumerating; . . .
_____ *v. t.* To count; to reckon; to ascertain the units of any sum, collection or multitude.
(Webster's 1828 *Dictionary*)

Numbers teach representation and name or represent quantities that are abstract (no unit of measure mentioned) or concrete (named unit of measure mentioned). There are at least fifteen (15) types of numbers distinguished in mathematics:

- cardinal
- ordinal
- determinate
- homogeneal
- integers
- rational
- irrational or surd
- fractional
- mixed
- prime
- perfect
- imperfect
- square
- cubic
- golden

3. **Numeration and Notation:**

numeration, *n.* [L. *numeratio.*] (1) The act or art of numbering. (2) In *arithmetic*, notation; the art of expressing in characters any number proposed in words, or of expressing in words any number proposed in characters; the act or art of writing or reading numbers.
(Webster's 1828 *Dictionary*)

notation, *n.* [L. *notatio*, from *noto*, to mark.] The act or practice of recording any thing by marks, figures or characters; particularly in arithmetic and algebra, the expressing of numbers and quantities by figures, signs or characters appropriate for the purpose.
(Webster's 1828 *Dictionary*)

Numeration and notation teach the correct reading and writing of numbers and quantities using place value.

4. **Measurement:**

measurement, *n.* The act of measuring; mensuration. **measure**, *v.t.* To take the dimensions of any thing; to compute or ascertain length, capacity or amount; to judge of distance, extent, or quantity; to ascertain degrees of heat or moisture. (Webster's 1828 *Dictionary*)

Measurement includes the teaching and learning of basic measurement in standard units of length, area, volume, value, weight, and time. The standard of measurement is Jesus Christ —the divine standard of excellence.

5. **Operations:**

addition, *n.* [L. *additio*, . . .] In *arithmetic*, the uniting of two or more numbers in one sum; also the rule or branch of arithmetic which treats of adding numbers. *Simple* addition is the joining of sums of the same denomination, as pounds to pounds, dollars to dollars. *Compound* addition is the joining of sums of different denominations, as dollars and cents. (Webster's 1828 *Dictionary*)

Notes

subtraction, *n*. [L. *subtractio.*] In *arithmetic*, the taking of a lesser number from a greater of the same kind or denomination; an operation by which is found the difference between two sums. (Webster's 1828 *Dictionary*)

multiplication, *n*. [L. *multiplicatio.*] In *arithmetic*, a rule or operation by which any given number may be increased according to any number of times proposed. Thus 10 multiplied by 5 is increased to 50. (Webster's 1828 *Dictionary*)

division, *n*. [L. *divisio.*] In *arithmetic*, the dividing of a number or quantity into any parts assigned; or the rule by which is found how many times one number is contained in another. (Webster's 1828 *Dictionary*)

The principles that govern mathematics reflect the three functions of government—I plan, I execute, and I evaluate.

6. Problem Solving:

solve, *v. t.* [L. *solvo*; . . .] Properly, to loosen or separate the parts of any thing; hence, to explain; to resolve; . . . to unfold; to clear up; as what is obscure or difficult to be understood; as to *solve* questions; to *solve* difficulties or a problem. (Webster's 1828 *Dictionary*)

problem, *n*. [Fr. *probleme*; . . . Gr. . . . to throw forward; . . . to throw, L. *pello.*] (1) A question proposed. (2) In *geometry*, a proposition in which some operation or construction is required, as to divide a line or an angle, to let fall a perpendicular, &c. (3) In *general*, any question involving doubt or uncertainty, and requiring some operation, experiment or further evidence for its solution. (Webster's 1828 *Dictionary*)

The practical meaning and purpose is given to the study of mathematics by enabling one to answer questions requiring some operation for its solution. "The Five-Step Method" provides a strategy for solving any problem (see pp. 110–111). It identifies the data and tools given to solve the problem; it identifies the problem; it analyzes (plans) and records the proposed procedure intended to solve the problem; it executes the proposed plan using numbers, signs, and units of measure; and it verifies the solution.

This year in my math class, I have gained a better understanding of numbers. Through learning definitions, I have found a greater value in math. They help everything to stay inside my head and help me understand the basic principles. This new understanding will help me from seventh grade through high school math. I enjoy math more than ever.

Katie D.
Sixth Grade, StoneBridge School
Chesapeake, Virginia

By using *Ray's Arithmetic*, I am able to understand and solve math problems more efficiently. It has helped me be more diligent in working out the problems using rules and principles. The rules and principles make the problems easier to solve. I have learned that I should set a high standard for myself in all things that I do and I am now able to do it through Jesus Christ.

Rachel C.
Sixth Grade, StoneBridge School
Chesapeake, Virginia

An American Christian Mathematics Curriculum Overview

As long as algebra is taught in school, there will be prayer in school.
(Cokie Roberts)

Grades K–4 *The Art of Computation* RightStart™ *Knowledge*	**Grades 5–7** *The Science of Numbers* Rays™ Arithmetics *Understanding*	**Grades 8–12** *Applied Mathematics* Individual Branches of Math *Wisdom*
Demonstrates and teaches the foundational principles of mathematics through *RightStart*™, a non-traditional American, abacus-based curriculum and the Principle Approach®. Teaches the science of quantity based upon Biblical principles. Introduces all branches of mathematics with a rich vocabulary that teaches students how to think mathematically. Emphasizes oral, mental, visual, kinesthetic, and linguistic activities for a lifetime love of mathematics. Cultivates American Christian character, emphasizing effort not talent, and builds scholarship for God-honoring problem solving. Places mathematics on the Chain of Christianity®, His Story of liberty.	Builds mastery and application of arithmetic skills for use in everyday life and leadership based upon *Ray's*™ *Arithmetics*, a highly successful nineteenth century curriculum. Teaches mathematical principles and logical thinking for problem solving in a wide range of useful and practical business transactions using the complete Notebook Method and the Principle Approach. Emphasizes mastery of math terms, mental math, notation, derivations of rules and formulas, and story problems. Cultivates American Christian character and scholarship for God-honoring problem solving. Places mathematics and mathematicians on the Chain of Christianity, His Story of liberty.	Teaches individual branches of mathematics, from algebra through calculus, for mastery of principles and application to technology and science using the Principle Approach and textbooks enriched with this perspective. Effectively teaches the coherence between abstract models and concrete reality, emphasizing both the deductive and intuitive characterization of mathematics. Cultivates American Christian character and scholarship for God-honoring problem solving for life and leadership. Places mathematics and mathematicians on the Chain of Christianity, His Story of liberty.

As I implemented the *RightStart*™ program in our kindergarten class the first year, I made several observations. My students were able to understand concepts that children in former years had not been able to grasp in other arithmetic programs. Although the use of manipulative materials and concrete learning were included to meet the developmental needs of four-year-olds in all the other math programs, *RightStart*™ has most effectively enabled the children to understand the quantity that a number represents, size relationships, and ordinal placement.

After using the *RightStart*™ program for several years, I have seen that even very young students are able to understand how arithmetic reveals the character and attributes of God. The attribute of order is illustrated as students sequence the days of the week and learn place value. Students exercise the principle, my conscience is my most sacred property, as they are taught to reason and disagree. The principle of representation is reinforced as students learn to use concrete materials to represent various quantities.

The children always look forward to arithmetic instruction and remain engaged in the lesson because they are individually involved and are given opportunities to think and discover various ways to solve a problem or express an answer.

Sheree Beale
Kindergarten Master Teacher, StoneBridge School
Chesapeake, Virginia

As I reflect on the opening of school last year, I am reminded of the anxiety I felt towards adopting a new mathematics curriculum for our middle school. As a new "student" of *Ray's*™ *Arithmetics*, I realized that I needed to approach this revived methodology with a teachable spirit. Growth only occurs when one is willing to change. My understanding of mathematics was refreshed as I began to analyze each of the key words and principles. My individual character was tested and refined as my heart and mind adjusted to the necessary changes in my thinking. The joy of seeing God's character revealed throughout the principles as well as the execution of them in all the subjects and daily responsibilities are just a few of the blessings I received. As a result, my love of learning was rekindled by this enriching study and opportunity to teach the program.

The students received a new understanding of God and His character. Their minds were daily exercised and individually challenged at their learning threshold. The continual building and mastery of the rich vocabulary has equipped each student with the proper tools for mastering the mathematics concepts. In this program, the application of the five-step method enables students to practice thinking mathematically. They are reasoning every day, which enhances the students' ability to think critically in other subjects as well. Witnessing the fresh understanding and new appreciation toward mathematics in the students has refreshed and inspired me!

I believe others will come to have a deeper appreciation for math as a result of using *Ray's*™ *Arithmetics*. The fruit evidenced in each student has identified the great value of implementing this math program.

Susan Cognion
Sixth Grade Teacher, StoneBridge School
Chesapeake, Virginia

Mathematics Curriculum Charts

The traditional (American) mathematics curriculum is entirely out of relation to the real exhibition of the mathematical spirit in modern thought, with the result that it remains satisfied with examples which are both silly and unsystematic. The effect which we want to produce on our pupils is to generate a capacity to apply ideas to the concrete universe.

(Alfred North Whitehead)

Kindergarten Mathematics Curriculum
The Art of Computation

Purposes

1. Reveal God and His divine nature and character through mathematics.
2. Identify and demonstrate the principles governing mathematics.
3. Reason from principles of mathematics and apply them to problem solving.
4. Teach the place of mathematics on the Chain of Christianity® moving westward.
5. Form the character of the American Christian mathematician.

Principles

1. God's Principle of Individuality
2. Principle of representation
3. Commutative principle of addition
4. Associative principle of addition
5. Principle of symmetry
6. Principle of place value

Definitions

1. Mathematics is the science of quantity; of whatever can be measured or numbered. (Webster's 1828 *Dictionary*)
2. Mathematics is the language of God expressed in creation, the patterns of which laid the structure of the universe and describe the laws of His handiwork.
3. Arithmetic is the science of numbers or the art of computation. The various operations of arithmetic are performed by addition, subtraction, multiplication, and division. (Webster's 1828 *Dictionary*)

"For since the creation of the world His invisible attributes, His eternal power and divine nature, have been clearly seen, being understood through what has been made." (Romans 1:20, NASB)

Objectives

1. Recognize the abacus as a computation tool.
2. Build mental competence and problem-solving skills.
3. Demonstrate the laws of addition.
4. Learn the vocabulary of mathematics and the meaning of zero.
5. Listen to hear quantity.
6. Subitize to recognize a quantity without counting.
7. Visualize to see quantity mentally.
8. Analyze to think mathematically.
9. Synthesize to engineer or construct quantities.
10. Relate the following to other subjects in the curriculum:
    - Mathematical games
    - Poems, arts and crafts, music and rhythmic exercises

Foundations

Theme: Tools designed by man which assisted him in the art of computation:

1. abacus
2. calculator
3. modern-day computer

Biblical Foundation:

"When the Most High divided to the nations their inheritance, when he separated the sons of Adam, he set the bounds of the people according to the number of the children of Israel." (Deuteronomy 32:8)

Hebrew etymology of the word *abacus* is "dust." "And the LORD God formed man of the dust of the ground, and breathed into his nostrils the breath of life; and man became a living soul." (Genesis 2:7)

Math on the Chain of Christianity: History of the art of computation: From the abacus to the computer, tools of computation

1. Noah, the art of computation in building the ark
2. Job, great revelation of the principles of mathematics in the foundation of the universe

Vocabulary

Key Words:

1. abacus
2. addition
3. arithmetic
4. computation
5. left
6. mathematics
7. rectangle
8. right
9. square
10. subtraction
11. triangle
12. zero

Curriculum Words:

1. balanced
2. between
3. cents
4. cone
5. consecutive
6. copy
7. dozen
8. eleven
9. ellipse
10. equal
11. equation
12. equilateral
13. feet
14. fractal
15. fraction
16. greater than
17. half
18. heavy
19. hexagon
20. hour-hand
21. inch
22. less
23. less than
24. long
25. longer
26. longest
27. middle
28. midnight
29. minute hand
30. noon
31. o'clock
32. octagon
33. ones
34. parallel
35. perpendicular
36. place value
37. plus
38. quadrilateral
39. quarter
40. rectangle
41. reflection
42. rhombus
43. sphere
44. symmetrical
45. ten
46. tessellating
47. twelve
48. unbalanced
49. weight
50. ¢ + =

Kindergarten Mathematics Curriculum
The Art of Computation

Methods

1. Applying Notebook Method: 4-R'ing (researching, reasoning, relating, recording)
2. Cardinal and ordinal counting
3. Comparing
4. Contrasting
5. Estimating
6. Graphing
7. Grouping
8. Matching
9. Measuring
10. Notating
11. Partitioning
12. Recognizing visual and auditory patterns
13. Sorting
14. Tallying
15. Translating
16. Using a timeline: Math on the Chain of Christianity®

Resources

Teacher:
1. Bible
2. *RightStart*™
3. Large abacus
4. *Activities for Learning*™
5. *Mathematics: Is God Silent?*, Nickel, 2001
6. *The Remarkable Record of Job*, Morris, 1988
7. Teacher mathematics notebook

Student:
1. Abacus
2. Geo-boards
3. Number cards
4. Place-value cards
5. Calculator
6. Clock
7. Slates
8. Tally sticks
9. Balance beam
10. Student mathematics notebook

Performance Accomplishments

Numbers:

Knows even numbers to 20 and odd numbers to 19. Skip-counts by twos to 30, by fives to 100, by tens to 100. Recognizes quantities 1 to 100 and represents them on an abacus. Arranges 31 objects into groups of tens. Divides objects into halves and fourths. Counts with cardinals and ordinals.

Numeration and Notation:

Correctly forms handwritten numerals as well as reads 0 through 100. Reads and writes place value to the hundreds. Reads and writes addition equations. Learns to graph.

Measurement:

Monetary: Knows value and name of penny, nickel, and dime. *Linear:* Determines length with nonstandard measure. *Time:* Knows days of week, months of year, tells time to the half hour. *Geometry:* Knows mathematical names of triangle, rectangle, square, and circle. Knows parallel and perpendicular lines and planes. Continues a pattern on a geo-board. Constructs triangles, quadrilaterals, and octagons. *Volume:* Compares volumes using various scales. *Weight:* Compares weights using a balance beam.

Operations:

Addition: Understands addition as combining parts to form a whole. Partitions numbers 3 to 10 into parts. Knows number combinations equal to 10. Knows number combinations up to 10.

Subtraction: Understands subtraction as a missing addend. Understands subtraction as separating a whole.

Problem Solving:

Solves problems using a two-digit number plus one through nine with no trading. Solves missing addend problems. Solves basic subtraction problems.

First Grade Mathematics Curriculum
The Art of Computation

Purposes

1. Reveal God and His divine nature and character through mathematics.
2. Identify and demonstrate the principles governing mathematics.
3. Reason from principles of mathematics and apply them to problem solving.
4. Teach the place of mathematics on the Chain of Christianity® moving westward.
5. Form the character of the American Christian mathematician.

Principles

1. God's Principle of Individuality
2. Principle of representation
3. Commutative principle of addition
4. Associative principle of addition
5. Principle of symmetry
6. Principle of place value

Definitions

1. Mathematics is the science of quantity; of whatever can be measured or numbered. (Webster's 1828 *Dictionary*)
2. Mathematics is the language of God expressed in creation, the patterns of which laid the structure of the universe and describe the laws of His handiwork.
3. Arithmetic is the science of numbers or the art of computation. The various operations of arithmetic are performed by addition, subtraction, multiplication, and division. (Webster's 1828 *Dictionary*)

"For since the creation of the world His invisible attributes, His eternal power and divine nature, have been clearly seen, being understood through what has been made." (Romans 1:20, NASB)

Objectives

(build on previous grade level)

1. Develop proficient use of the abacus as a computation tool.
2. Increase mental mathematical competence and problem-solving skills.
3. Demonstrate the associative and commutative principles of addition.
4. Master the vocabulary of mathematics.
5. Recognize given quantities.
6. Change quantities.
7. Read quantities.
8. Partition quantities.
9. Relate the following to other subjects in the curriculum:
   - Mathematical games
   - Poems, arts and crafts, music and rhythmic exercises

Foundations

Theme: Applying the art of computation to navigation (the science of directing and measuring the course of ships or aircraft by the laws of geometry or by astronomical principles)

Biblical Foundation:

"It is he that sitteth upon the circle of the earth." (Isaiah 40:22)

"He has inscribed a circle on the surface of the waters, At the boundary of light and darkness." (Job 26:10, NASB)

"They that go down to the sea in ships, that do business in great waters; These see the works of the LORD." (Psalm 107:23–24)

Math on the Chain of Christianity: History of the art of computation applied to navigation

1. Johannes Kepler (1571–1630), three laws of planetary motion
2. Leonardo da Vinci (1452–1519), the invention of the mechanical calculator

Vocabulary

(build on previous grade level)

Key Words:

1. change
2. inch
3. minus
4. perimeter
5. subtract

Curriculum Words:

1. congruent
2. diagonal
3. flipping horizontally and vertically
4. line of symmetry
5. pentagon
6. reflection
7. symmetry

First Grade Mathematics Curriculum
The Art of Computation

Methods

1. Agreeing and disagreeing agreeably
2. Applying Notebook Method: 4-R'ing (researching, reasoning, relating, recording)
3. Comparing
4. Contrasting
5. Estimating
6. Graphing
7. Grouping
8. Matching
9. Measuring
10. Notating
11. Partitioning
12. Recognizing visual and auditory patterns
13. Reflecting
14. Sorting
15. Summarizing
16. Tallying
17. Translating
18. Using a timeline: Math on the Chain of Christianity®

Resources

Teacher:

1. Bible
2. *RightStart*™
3. Large abacus
4. *Activities for Learning*™
5. *Mathematics: Is God Silent?*, Nickel, 2001
6. Teacher mathematics notebook

Student:

1. Bible
2. Abacus
3. Geo-boards, number and place-value cards
4. Calculator
5. Clock and clock cards
6. Slates, tally sticks, and balance beam
7. Student mathematics notebook

Performance Accomplishments

(build on the previous year)

Numbers:

Knows even and odd numbers to 100. Knows even and odd adding rules. Skip-counts by twos, fives, and tens. Recognizes quantities 1 through 1000 and represents them on an abacus. Divides into halves, thirds, fourths, fifths, and sixths.

Numeration and Notation:

Reads and writes place value to the thousands. Reads and writes addition and subtraction equations. Graphs class and personal timekeeping information.

Measurement:

Monetary: Knows value and name of quarter. Adds values of several coins. Makes change. *Linear:* Determine length with nonstandard measure and inches. Knows what perimeter is and how to calculate one. *Time:* Knows the number of days in a week, a month, a year, and leap year. Knows the months of the year. Tells time to the minute. *Geometry:* Makes 10s, 100s, and 1000s for tens' fractal. Knows right angle, right triangle, congruence, and symmetry. Continues a pattern on a geo-board. Constructs quantities. *Volume:* Compares volumes using various scales. *Weight:* Weight comparison using a balance beam.

Operations:

Addition: Knows addition sums through 18 using non-counting strategies. Adds two four-digit numbers. Adds using more than two addends. *Subtraction:* Knows subtraction as a missing addend and as going up as well as going down.

Problem Solving:

Adds two-digit numbers mentally. Subtracts two-digit numbers mentally. Checks addition and subtraction. Solves simple money problems. Adds with more than two addends. Solves missing addend problems. Solves basic subtraction problems.

Second Grade Mathematics Curriculum
The Art of Computation

Purposes

1. Reveal God and His divine nature and character through mathematics.
2. Identify and demonstrate the principles governing mathematics.
3. Reason from principles of mathematics and apply them to problem solving.
4. Teach the place of mathematics on the Chain of Christianity® moving westward.
5. Form the character of the American Christian mathematician.

Principles

1. God's Principle of Individuality
2. Principle of representation
3. Commutative principle of addition
4. Associative principle of addition
5. Principle of symmetry
6. Principle of place value

Definitions

1. Mathematics is the science of quantity; of whatever can be measured or numbered. (Webster's 1828 *Dictionary*)
2. Mathematics is the language of God expressed in creation, the patterns of which laid the structure of the universe and describe the laws of His handiwork.
3. Arithmetic is the science of numbers or the art of computation. The various operations of arithmetic are performed by addition, subtraction, multiplication, and division. (Webster's 1828 *Dictionary*)

"For since the creation of the world His invisible attributes, His eternal power and divine nature, have been clearly seen, being understood through what has been made." (Romans 1:20, NASB)

Objectives

(build on previous grade level)

1. Increase mental mathematical competence and problem-solving skills.
2. Demonstrate the associative and commutative principles of addition.
3. Continue learning the vocabulary of mathematics.
4. Express reasoning using Venn diagrams and a math journal.
5. Understand addition and subtraction strategies.
6. Reason inductively using Roman numerals.
7. Solve integer and fraction problems.
8. Identify the relation between addition and multiplication.
9. Relate the following to other subjects in the curriculum:
   - Mathematical games
   - Poems, arts and crafts, and music
   - Engineering tools

Foundations

Theme: Applying the art of computation to keeping time and designing machines

Biblical Foundation:

"So teach us to number our days, That we may present to You a heart of wisdom." (Psalm 90:12, NASB)

"And God said, Let there be lights in the firmament of the heaven to divide the day from the night; and let them be for signs, and for seasons, and for days, and years:" (Genesis 1:14)

Math on the Chain of Christianity: History of the art of computation: From the abacus to the computer; timekeeping machines

1. Blaise Pascal (1623–62), invented the arithmetic machine, the first digital calculator.
2. Christiaan Huygens (1629–95), designed the pendulum clock.

Vocabulary

(build on previous grade level)

Key Words:

1. area
2. clockwise
3. difference
4. dollar
5. double
6. foot
7. horizontal
8. mile
9. minuend
10. product
11. remainder
12. strategy
13. subtrahend
14. vertical

Curriculum Words:

1. A.M. and P.M.
2. annex
3. centimeter
4. consecutive
5. counter-clockwise
6. decimal point
7. digit
8. equinox
9. half dollar
10. hexagon
11. multiple
12. rhombus, rhombi
13. square centimeter
14. square inch
15. sunrise
16. sunset
17. tangram
18. tetrahedron
19. vertex, vertices

Second Grade Mathematics Curriculum
The Art of Computation

Methods

1. Agreeing and disagreeing agreeably
2. Applying Notebook Method: 4-R'ing (researching, reasoning, relating, recording)
3. Comparing
4. Contrasting
5. Converting
6. Drawing
7. Engineering
8. Estimating
9. Graphing
10. Grouping
11. Journaling
12. Matching
13. Measuring
14. Notating
15. Partitioning
16. Recognizing visual and auditory patterns
17. Reflecting
18. Sorting
19. Summarizing
20. Tallying
21. Translating
22. Using a timeline: Math on the Chain of Christianity®

Resources

Teacher:

1. Bible
2. *RightStart*™
3. Large abacus
4. *Activities for Learning*™
5. *Mathematics: Is God Silent?*, Nickel, 2001
6. Teacher mathematics notebook

Student:

1. Bible
2. Abacus
3. Geo-boards
4. Number and place-value cards
5. Calculator, clock, slates, and tally sticks
6. Balance beam and minute cards
7. Drawing tools
8. Games: Subtraction Chain, Fraction, and Corner
9. Tangram puzzles
10. 100 charts and fraction charts
11. Student mathematics notebook

Performance Accomplishments

(build on the previous year)

Numbers:

Understands fractions as a type of division. Knows unit fractions up to $^1/_{10}$. Understands mixed numbers (i.e., 1½).

Numeration and Notation:

Skip-counts twos to tens to the first ten multiples. Reads and constructs Roman numerals to 4,999. Reads and writes addition and subtraction, multiplication and division equations. Constructs geometric shapes using a compass, 30°–60° triangle, and T-square. Graphs temperature readings.

Measurement:

Monetary: Solves simple money problems using decimals. *Linear:* Determines length by using a ruler in inches and centimeters. Knows what perimeter and area are and how to calculate each. Finds area in square inches or square centimeters. *Time:* Tells time to the minute. *Geometry:* Constructs an equilateral triangle with drawing tools. Finds multiple solutions for tangram problems. Understands line symmetry. *Volume:* Compares volumes using various scales. *Weight:* Compares weights using a balance beam.

Operations:

Addition: Adds two-digit numbers mentally. Adds four-digit numbers. Knows addition facts. *Subtraction:* Understands subtraction. Subtracts two-digit numbers mentally. Subtracts four-digit numbers. Knows subtraction facts. *Multiplication:* Understands multiplication. Knows multiplication facts and multiplies four-digit numbers by one-digit numbers and then by two-digit numbers.

Problem Solving:

Solves problems in more than one way. Works well individually or in a group to solve problems. Uses a calculator to add, subtract, and multiply whole numbers.

Third Grade Mathematics Curriculum
The Art of Computation

Purposes

1. Reveal God and His divine nature and character through mathematics.
2. Identify and demonstrate the principles governing mathematics.
3. Reason from principles of mathematics and apply them to problem solving.
4. Teach the place of mathematics on the Chain of Christianity® moving westward.
5. Form the character of the American Christian mathematician.

Principles

1. God's Principle of Individuality
2. Principle of representation
3. Commutative principle of addition
4. Associative principle of addition
5. Principle of symmetry
6. Principle of place value

Definitions

1. Mathematics is the science of quantity; of whatever can be measured or numbered. (Webster's 1828 *Dictionary*)
2. Mathematics is the language of God expressed in creation, the patterns of which laid the structure of the universe and describe the laws of His handiwork.
3. Arithmetic is the science of numbers or the art of computation. The various operations of arithmetic are performed by addition, subtraction, multiplication, and division. (Webster's 1828 *Dictionary*)

"For since the creation of the world His invisible attributes, His eternal power and divine nature, have been clearly seen, being understood through what has been made." (Romans 1:20, NASB)

Objectives

(build on previous grade level)

1. Develop proficiency in the associative, commutative, and distributive principles of mathematics.
2. Solve calendar problems.
3. Construct bar graphs comparing growth, area, and population.
4. Solve array (area) problems.
5. Perform multi-digit subtraction with borrowing.
6. Read and interpret various measurement scales.
7. Perform multiplication algorithm.
8. Begin division by small numbers.
9. Attain proficiency in mental mathematical competence and problem-solving skills.
10. Continue learning the vocabulary of mathematics.
11. Relate the following to other subjects in the curriculum:
    - Mathematical games
    - Poems, arts and crafts, and music
    - Drawing tools.

Foundations

Theme: Applying the art of computation to the basic laws of physics

Biblical Foundation:

"He stretches out the north over empty space And hangs the earth on nothing." (Job 26:7, NASB)

"Oh that I had wings like a dove! for then would I fly away, and be at rest." (Psalm 55:6)

Math on the Chain of Christianity: History of the art of computation: Application of computation to the laws of physics

1. Sir Isaac Newton (1642–1727), the Universal Law of Gravitation (down)
2. Daniel Bernoulli (1700–82), the Law of Hydrodynamic Pressure leads to the principle of flight (up)

Vocabulary

(build on previous grade level)

Key Words:

1. divisor
2. dividend
3. gallon
4. ounces
5. quart
6. quotient
7. remainder

Curriculum Words:

1. cube
2. rotation
3. 90°
4. 180°
5. 270°
6. 360°

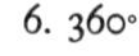

Third Grade Mathematics Curriculum
The Art of Computation

Methods

1. Agreeing and disagreeing agreeably
2. Applying Notebook Method: 4-R'ing (researching, reasoning, relating, recording)
3. Comparing
4. Contrasting
5. Converting
6. Drawing
7. Engineering
8. Estimating
9. Graphing
10. Grouping
11. Journaling
12. Matching
13. Measuring
14. Notating
15. Partitioning
16. Recognizing visual patterns
17. Reflecting
18. Sorting
19. Summarizing
20. Tallying
21. Translating
22. Using a timeline: Math on the Chain of Christianity®

Resources

Teacher:

1. Bible
2. *RightStart*™
3. Large abacus
4. *Activities for Learning*™
5. *Mathematics: Is God Silent?*, Nickel, 2001
6. Teacher mathematics notebook

Student:

1. Bible
2. Number and fraction cards
3. 1″ tiles and plastic coins
4. Calculator, clock, and slates
5. Drawing tools
6. Multiplication and division games
7. Corner game
8. Four-in-one and pro rulers
9. Student mathematics notebook

Performance Accomplishments

(build on the previous year)

Numbers:

Understands fractions as a type of division. Knows unit fractions up to $^1/_{10}$. Understands mixed numbers (i.e., 1½). Knows ½ and ¼ of various quantities.

Numeration and Notation:

Skip-counts twos to tens for the first ten multiples. Reads and writes numbers to one million. Reads and interprets various scaled data. Performs image rotation. Reads and writes large numbers (greater than four digits). Constructs geometric shapes using compass, 30°–60° triangle, and T-square. Constructs bar graphs displaying and comparing data (i.e., growth, population, area). Draws geometric figures. Reads and writes time in various ways (i.e., musical notes).

Measurement:

Monetary: Solves simple money problems using decimals and makes change for amounts less than one dollar. *Linear:* Determines length using a ruler in inches and centimeters. Knows what perimeter and area are and how to calculate each. Finds area in square inches or square centimeters. *Time*: Tells time to the minute. *Geometry:* Constructs an equilateral triangle with drawing tools. Finds multiple solutions for tangram problems. Understands line symmetry. Understands the concept of an angle. Constructs and reads bar graphs. *Volume:* Compares volume using various scales. *Weight:* Understands weight.

Operations:

Addition: Adds two-digit numbers mentally. Adds several four-digit numbers. Knows addition facts. *Subtraction:* Understands subtraction. Subtracts two-digit numbers mentally. Subtracts four-digit numbers. Knows subtraction combinations. *Multiplication:* Understands multiplication. Knows multiplication facts. Multiplies four-digit by two-digit numbers. Knows multiplication combinations. *Division:* Understands division as inverse of multiplication. Solves division story problems with remainders.

Problem Solving:

Solves a problem in more than one way. Works well individually or in a group to solve problems. Uses a calculator to add, subtract, multiply, and divide whole numbers, fractions, and mixed numbers. Solves multi-step problems.

Fourth Grade Mathematics Curriculum
The Art of Computation

Purposes

1. Reveal God and His divine nature and character through mathematics.
2. Identify and demonstrate the principles governing mathematics.
3. Reason from principles of mathematics and apply them to problem solving.
4. Teach the place of mathematics on the Chain of Christianity® moving westward.
5. Form the character of the American Christian mathematician.

Principles

1. God's Principle of Individuality
2. Principle of representation
3. Commutative principle of addition
4. Associative principle of addition
5. Principle of symmetry
6. Principle of place value

Definitions

1. Mathematics is the science of quantity; of whatever can be measured or numbered. (Webster's 1828 *Dictionary*)
2. Mathematics is the language of God expressed in creation, the patterns of which laid the structure of the universe and describe the laws of His handiwork.
3. Arithmetic is the science of numbers or the art of computation. The various operations of arithmetic are performed by addition, subtraction, multiplication, and division. (Webster's 1828 *Dictionary*)

"For since the creation of the world His invisible attributes, His eternal power and divine nature, have been clearly seen, being understood through what has been made." (Romans 1:20, NASB)

Objectives

(build on previous grade level)

1. Begin the study of the science of numbers.
2. Attain proficiency in associative, commutative, and distributive principles of mathematics.
3. Develop and use algebraic thinking.
4. Apply percentage with time (calculate interest, mortgage, etc.) and without the element of time (calculate discounts, etc.).
5. Attain competence in measuring with the metric system.
6. Continue learning the vocabulary of mathematics.
7. Relate the following to other subjects in the curriculum:
   - Mathematical games
   - Poems, arts and crafts, and music
   - Drawing tools

Foundations

Theme: Applying the art of computation to mathematics and physics

Biblical Foundation:

"Those who go down to the sea in ships, Who do business on great waters; They have seen the works of the LORD, And His wonders in the deep." (Psalm 107:23–24, NASB)

Math on the Chain of Christianity: History of the art of computation: Application of computation to the laws of physics

1. Nathaniel Bowditch (1773–1838), Father of American Mathematics; wrote the "seaman's bible on navigation"; lunars
2. Michael Faraday (1791–1867), the Law of Electromagnetic Induction

Vocabulary

Key Words:

1. cylinder
2. improper fraction
3. percent
4. prime number
5. prism

Curriculum Words:

1. coordinate plane
2. protractor
3. pyramid
4. rotational symmetry
5. sphere
6. square
7. square root

Fourth Grade Mathematics Curriculum
The Art of Computation

Methods

1. Agreeing and disagreeing agreeably
2. Applying Notebook Method: 4-R'ing (researching, reasoning, relating, recording)
3. Comparing
4. Contrasting
5. Converting
6. Drawing
7. Engineering
8. Estimating
9. Graphing
10. Grouping
11. Journaling
12. Matching
13. Measuring
14. Notating
15. Partitioning
16. Recognizing visual patterns
17. Reflecting
18. Sorting
19. Summarizing
20. Tallying
21. Translating
22. Using a timeline: Math on the Chain of Christianity®

Resources

Teacher:

1. Bible
2. *RightStart*™
3. Large abacus
4. *Activities for Learning*™
5. *Mathematics: Is God Silent?*, Nickel, 2001
6. Teacher mathematics notebook

Student:

1. Bible
2. Number and fraction cards
3. 1″ tiles and plastic coins
4. Calculator, clock, and slates
5. Drawing tools and T-square
6. Multiplication and division games
7. Corner game and tangram puzzles
8. Four-in-one and pro rulers
9. 30°–60° triangle
10. Student mathematics notebook

Performance Accomplishments

(build on the previous year)

Numbers:

Understands decimals to two places. Understands and uses prime numbers. Factors numbers into primes. Understands and uses simple percents. Adds and subtracts simple fractions. Converts between improper fractions and mixed fractions.

Numeration and Notation:

Reads and writes numbers to 999 million. Reads and interprets various scaled data. Reads and writes large numbers (greater than 4 digits). Constructs geometric shapes using a compass, 30°–60° triangle, and T-square. Collects and displays data using bar graphs and pie charts.

Measurement:

Monetary: Solves producer/consumer problems involving money. *Linear:* Determines length using a ruler to fourths and tenths of an inch, tenths of a centimeter. Finds area to tenths of square inches or square centimeter. *Geometry:* Uses a protractor. Sketches three-dimensional shapes. Understands rotational symmetry. Finds the area of a triangle. Locates points on a coordinate system. Constructs and reads pie graphs.

Operations:

Division: Solves division story problems with remainders. Divides four-digit numbers by one-digit numbers using short division. Understands and determines averages. Knows division combinations.

Problem Solving:

Uses a calculator to find squares and square roots. Divides and makes sense of the remainder using a calculator. Justifies one's own reasoning. Determines the probability of an event.

Fifth Grade Mathematics Curriculum
The Science of Numbers

Purposes

1. Reveal God and His divine nature and character through mathematics.
2. Identify and demonstrate the principles governing mathematics.
3. Reason from principles of mathematics and apply them to problem solving.
4. Teach the place of mathematics on the Chain of Christianity® moving westward.
5. Form the character of the American Christian mathematician.

Principles

1. God's Principle of Individuality
2. Principle of representation
3. Commutative principle of addition
4. Associative principle of addition
5. Principle of symmetry
6. Principle of place value

Definitions

1. Mathematics is the science of quantity; of whatever can be measured or numbered. (Webster's 1828 *Dictionary*)
2. Mathematics is the language of God expressed in creation, the patterns of which laid the structure of the universe and describe the laws of His handiwork.
3. Arithmetic is the science of numbers or the art of computation. The various operations of arithmetic are performed by addition, subtraction, multiplication, and division. (Webster's 1828 *Dictionary*)

"For since the creation of the world His invisible attributes, His eternal power and divine nature, have been clearly seen, being understood through what has been made." (Romans 1:20, NASB)

Objectives

(build on previous grade level)

1. Continue the study of the science of numbers.
2. Attain proficiency in associative, commutative, and distributive principles of mathematics.
3. Develop and use algebraic thinking.
4. Apply percentage with and without the element of time.
5. Attain competence in measuring with the metric system.
6. Increase the vocabulary of mathematics.
7. Relate the following to other subjects in the curriculum:
   - Mathematical games
   - Poems, crafts, and music
   - Engineering tools and projects
   - Local businesses
   - Local newspapers: bank ads, sale ads, and finance section

Foundations

Theme: History of the science of numbers and the application to the sciences, invention, and enterprise

Biblical Foundation:

"Where were you when I laid the foundation of the earth? Tell Me, if you have understanding, Who set its measurements? Since you know. Or who stretched the line on it? On what were its bases sunk? Or who laid its cornerstone?" (Job 38:4–6, NASB)

Math on the Chain of Christianity: History of the science of numbers and God's purpose for the westward move of the Gospel

1. George Washington (1732–99), the application of geometry to surveying
2. Charles Babbage (1791?–1871), invented the difference machine and the analytical engine.

Vocabulary

(build on previous grade level)

Key Words:

1. acre
2. ar
3. average
4. base
5. cancellation
6. circumference
7. diameter
8. exponent
9. gram
10. hundredths
11. latitude
12. liter
13. longitude
14. meter
15. mile
16. radius
17. rate
18. rod
19. tenths
20. thousandths

Curriculum Words:

1. acute
2. altitude
3. arithmetic
4. asset
5. average
6. bankrupt
7. bond
8. centiliter
9. centimeter
10. commission
11. concave
12. convex
13. currency
14. cylinder
15. decimeter
16. discount
17. exponent
18. hectare
19. interest
20. kilometer
21. liability
22. loss
23. millimeter
24. obtuse
25. premium
26. principal
27. profit
28. real estate
29. retail
30. stock
31. stockholder
32. tax
33. trapezium
34. trapezoid

Fifth Grade Mathematics Curriculum
The Science of Numbers

Methods

1. Agreeing and disagreeing agreeably
2. Applying Notebook Method: 4-R'ing (researching, reasoning, relating, recording)
3. Comparing
4. Contrasting
5. Converting
6. Drawing
7. Engineering
8. Estimating
9. Graphing
10. Grouping
11. Journaling
12. Matching
13. Measuring
14. Partitioning
15. Recognizing visual patterns
16. Sorting
17. Summarizing
18. Tallying
19. Translating
20. Using a timeline: Math on the Chain of Christianity®

Resources

Teacher:

1. Bible
2. *Ray's™ New Practical Arithmetic,* Ray, 1985
3. *Mathematics: Is God Silent?,* Nickel, 2001
4. *Men of Mathematics,* Bell, 1965
5. Teacher mathematics notebook
6. Local banks, stock brokers, financial analysts, bookkeepers, tax agencies, economists

Student:

1. Bible
2. *Ray's™ New Practical Arithmetic,* Ray, 1985
3. Calculator
4. Drawing tools
5. Tangram puzzles
6. Student mathematics notebook

Performance Accomplishments

(build on the previous year)

Numbers:

Understands decimals to four places. Uses percent with or without the element of time. Adds and subtracts simple fractions. Reduces fractions, decimals, and percents. Squares and cubes numbers. Manually extracts the square root of numbers with up to nine digits. Solves simple problems involving compound denominate numbers. Groups numbers into orders through the first twelve periods (units through decillion). Calculates a base, rate, or percentage when two of the three terms are given. Applies percentage to mercantile and stock transactions. Applies percentage to interest, discount, exchange, insurance, and taxes.

Numeration and Notation:

Reads and writes numbers using the Arabic system of notation up to 999 decillions. Reads and interprets various scaled data. Constructs geometric shapes using a compass, 30°–60° triangle, and T-square. Collects and displays data using bar graphs and pie charts. Reads and writes numbers up to 4,999 using the Roman system of notation.

Measurement:

Monetary: Solves producer/consumer problems using U.S. currency. *Linear:* Measures, converts, reduces, and solves simple practical problems using the English and the metric systems of measurement. *Geometry:* Uses a protractor. Sketches three-dimensional shapes. Understands rotational symmetry. Finds the perimeter and area of a triangle, circle, and solid. Locates points on a coordinate system. Constructs and reads pie graphs. Measures lines, angles, surfaces, and solids. *Time*: Calculates time corresponding to any difference of longitude. Calculates longitude corresponding to any difference of time.

Operations:

Addition: Adds from two to fifteen addends with up to nine digits in each addend. Adds decimal fractions. Adds using the metric system of measurement. *Subtraction:* Subtracts numbers having minuends of up to eleven digits and subtrahends of up to eleven digits with or without borrowing. *Multiplication*: Multiplies five-digit by four-digit numbers. *Division*: Divides six-digit numbers by twelve or less using mental short division. Divides six-digit numbers by three-digit numbers using long division. Understands and finds averages.

Problem Solving:

Calculates squares, square roots, cubes, and cube roots manually or with a calculator. Solves story problems making use of any combination of addition, subtraction, multiplication, and division using the five-step method to problem solving applied to measurement and percent. Justifies one's own reasoning. Solves simple problems of compound denominate numbers, integers, fractions, and decimal fractions. Solves linear, square, cubic, time, and monetary story problems.

Sixth Grade Mathematics Curriculum
The Science of Numbers

Purposes

1. Reveal God and His divine nature and character through mathematics.
2. Identify and demonstrate the principles governing mathematics.
3. Reason from principles of mathematics and apply them to problem solving.
4. Teach the place of mathematics on the Chain of Christianity® moving westward.
5. Form the character of the American Christian mathematician.

Principles

1. God's Principle of Individuality
2. Principle of representation
3. Commutative principle of addition
4. Associative principle of addition
5. Principle of symmetry
6. Principle of place value

Definitions

1. Mathematics is the science of quantity; of whatever can be measured or numbered. (Webster's 1828 *Dictionary*)
2. Mathematics is the language of God expressed in creation, the patterns of which laid the structure of the universe and describe the laws of His handiwork.
3. Arithmetic is the science of numbers or the art of computation. The various operations of arithmetic are performed by addition, subtraction, multiplication, and division. (Webster's 1828 *Dictionary*)

"For since the creation of the world His invisible attributes, His eternal power and divine nature, have been clearly seen, being understood through what has been made." (Romans 1:20, NASB)

Objectives

(build on previous grade level)

1. Attain proficiency in the science of numbers.
2. Attain proficiency in the associative, commutative, and distributive principles of mathematics.
3. Master the use of mathematics vocabulary.
4. Attain proficiency in Arabic and Roman numeration and notation.
5. Attain proficiency in algebraic thinking.
6. Attain proficiency in casting out nines to prove the four operations.
7. Apply percentage with and without the element of time to business transactions.
8. Attain proficiency in alligation.
9. Attain proficiency using the metric system.
10. Receive introduction to computer-assisted design (CAD) software.
11. Relate the following to other subjects in the curriculum:
    - Mathematical games
    - Poems, crafts, and music
    - Engineering tools and projects
    - Local businesses
    - Local newspapers: bank ads, sale ads, and finance stocks and bonds section
    - Computer laboratory, CAD software, computerized graphing software

Foundations

Theme: History of mathematics and the application of mathematical principles to science

Biblical Foundation:

"Come," said Jesus. Then Peter got out of the boat and started walking toward Jesus across the water, but as soon as he felt the force of the wind, he took fright and began to sink. "Lord! Save me!" he cried. Jesus put out his hand at once and held him. "Man of little faith," he said, "why did you doubt?" And as they got into the boat the wind dropped. The men in the boat bowed down before him and said, "Truly, you are the Son of God." (Matthew 14:29–33, Jerusalem Bible)

Math on the Chain of Christianity: History of mathematics, Creation to the Reformation

1. Pythagoras (582?–500? B.C.), coined the term *mathematics*, contributed the proof and Pythagorean Theory.
2. Archimedes of Syracuse (287–212 B.C.), the principle of buoyancy.
3. Roger Bacon (1214–94?), introduced Arabic numerals in Europe.
4. Fibonacci (Leonardo de Pisa) (1180–1250), the occurrence of Fibonacci numbers and the Golden Section Ratio, *phi*.

Vocabulary

(build on previous grade level)

Key Words:

1. accounts
2. aliquot parts
3. balance
4. bookkeeping
5. Celsius
6. centigrade
7. credit
8. debit
9. Fahrenheit
10. greatest common divisor
11. least common multiple
12. ledger
13. loan
14. proportion
15. ratio

Curriculum Words:

1. annual interest
2. annuity
3. antecedent
4. assessor
5. compound interest
6. consequent
7. consignment
8. customs
9. duty
10. foreign exchange
11. investment
12. invoice
13. loan
14. progressions
15. promissory note
16. revenue
17. series
18. tariff

Sixth Grade Mathematics Curriculum
The Science of Numbers

Methods

1. Agreeing and disagreeing agreeably
2. Applying Notebook Method: 4-R'ing (researching, reasoning, relating, recording)
3. Comparing
4. Contrasting
5. Conversing with professionals in the field
6. Converting
7. Defining
8. Drawing
9. Engineering
10. Estimating
11. Extending
12. Field study tours
13. Graphing
14. Grouping
15. Journaling
16. Matching
17. Measuring
18. Notating
19. Partitioning
20. Practicing practical problems
21. Proving
22. Recognizing visual patterns
23. Reducing
24. Reflecting
25. Sketching
26. Sorting
27. Summarizing
28. Tallying
29. Translating
30. Using a timeline: Math on the Chain of Christianity®
31. Using various tools of mathematicians, i.e., calculators and computers

Resources

Teacher:

1. Bible
2. *Ray's™ New Higher Arithmetic*, Ray, 1985
3. *Mathematics: Is God Silent?*, Nickel, 2001
4. *Men of Mathematics*, Bell, 1965
5. Teacher mathematics notebook
6. Local banks, stock brokers, financial analysts, bookkeepers, tax agencies, economists
7. Computerized software packages related to budgeting, profit & loss statements, balance sheets, computer labs, computerized graphing, and probability software

Students:

1. Bible
2. *Ray's™ New Higher Arithmetic*, Ray, 1985
3. Calculator
4. Computer, CAD software, and software packages relating to business transactions
5. Drawing tools
6. Mathematical games and tangram puzzles
7. Student mathematics notebook

Performance Accomplishments

(build on the previous year)

Numbers:

Understands decimals to billionths. Thoroughly understands and uses percentages with or without the element of time. Proficiently uses the four operations on simple, complex, and compound fractions. Reduces fractions, decimals, and percents. Squares and cubes numbers. Manually extracts the square root of a number having up to nine digits. Proficiently solves problems involving compound denominate numbers. Groups numbers into orders through the first twenty-two periods (units through vigintillions). Thoroughly understands the properties and kinds of numbers and the principles and rules that relate to them.

Numeration and Notation:

Reads and writes numbers using the Arabic system of numeration and notation up to 999 vigintillions. Reads and interprets various scaled data. Constructs geometric shapes using a compass, 30°–60° triangle, and T-square. Collects and displays data using bar graphs and pie charts. Reads and writes numbers up to 4,999,000 using the Roman system of notation. Operates CAD software to solve simple engineering or design problems.

Measurement:

Monetary: Solves producer/consumer problems using U.S. currency. *Linear:* Measures, converts, reduces, and solves simple practical problems using the English and the metric systems of measurement. *Geometry:* Uses a protractor. Sketches three-dimensional shapes. Understands rotational symmetry. Finds the perimeter and area of a triangle, circle, and solid. Locates points on a coordinate system. Constructs and reads pie graphs. Can measure lines, angles, surfaces, and solids. *Time*: Calculates time corresponding to any difference of longitude, and calculates longitude corresponding to any difference of time.

Operations:

Addition: Proficiently calculates manually or with the aid of an abacus, calculator, or computer, sums with more than fifteen addends, with or without decimals. Proficiently adds fractions and decimal fractions. Proficiently adds metrically. *Subtraction:* Proficiently subtracts numbers having minuends larger than eleven digits and subtrahends larger than eleven digits, with or without borrowing and with or without decimals. *Multiplication*: Proficiently calculates products, manually or with the aid of a calculating device after mastery, using factors greater than five digits, with or without decimals in the Arabic or the metric systems. *Division*: Proficiently divides numbers mentally using short or long division in the Arabic or the metric systems. Understands aliquots and alligation.

Problem Solving:

Proficiently calculates squares, square roots, cubes, and cube roots manually or with a calculator. Proficiently solves multi-step story problems making use of any combination of addition, subtraction, multiplication, and division using the five-step method to problem solving applied to measurement, percent, compound denominate numbers, ratio, and proportion. Justifies one's own reasoning using the five-step method to problem solving.

Seventh Grade Mathematics Curriculum
The Science of Numbers

Purposes

1. Reveal God and His divine nature and character through mathematics.
2. Identify and demonstrate the principles governing mathematics.
3. Reason from the principles of mathematics and apply them to problem solving.
4. Teach the place of mathematics on the Chain of Christianity® moving westward.
5. Form the character of the American Christian mathematician.

Principles

1. God's Principle of Individuality
2. Principle of representation
3. Commutative principle of addition
4. Associative principle of addition
5. Principle of symmetry
6. Principle of place value

Definitions

1. Mathematics is the science of quantity; of whatever can be measured or numbered. (Webster's 1828 *Dictionary*)
2. Mathematics is the language of God expressed in creation, the patterns of which laid the structure of the universe and describe the laws of His handiwork.
3. Arithmetic is the science of numbers or the art of computation. The various operations of arithmetic are performed by addition, subtraction, multiplication, and division. (Webster's 1828 *Dictionary*)

"For since the creation of the world His invisible attributes, His eternal power and divine nature, have been clearly seen, being understood through what has been made." (Romans 1:20, NASB)

Objectives

(build on previous grade level)

1. Build toward mastering the art of computation and the science of numbers.
2. Master use of the associative, commutative, and distributive principles.
3. Master use of mathematical terms.
4. Master notation of Arabic and Roman numeration systems.
5. Master applying percentage with and without the element of time to business transactions.
6. Master using the English and metric systems of measurement.
7. Attain proficient use of computer-assisted design (CAD) software.
8. Attain proficiency in algebraic thinking.
9. Relate the following to other subjects in the curriculum:
   - Mathematical games
   - Poems, crafts, and music
   - Engineering tools and projects
   - Local businesses
   - Local newspapers: bank ads, sale ads, and finance stocks and bonds section
   - Computer laboratory, CAD software, computerized graphing software

Foundations

Theme: History of mathematics and the application of mathematical principles to science and technology

Biblical Foundation:

"When I consider Your heavens, the work of Your fingers, the moon and the stars, which You have ordained; What is man that You take thought of him, and the son of man that You care for him?" (Psalm 8:3–4, NASB)

Math on the Chain of Christianity: History of modern mathematics, Reformation to the present

1. Galileo Galilei (1564–1642), geometric and military compasses
2. Blaise Pascal (1623–62), the arithmetic machine and the Pascal Triangle
3. Karl Gauss (1777–1855), "prince of mathematicians," aided the development of systematic arithmetic.
4. Georg Cantor (1845–1918), "The essence of mathematics resides in its freedom."

Vocabulary

(build on previous grade level)

Key Words:

1. accounts
2. aliquot parts
3. balance
4. bookkeeping
5. Celsius
6. centigrade
7. credit
8. debit
9. Fahrenheit
10. greatest common divisor
11. least common multiple
12. ledger
13. loan
14. proportion
15. ratio

Curriculum Words:

1. annual interest
2. annuity
3. antecedent
4. assessor
5. compound interest
6. consequent
7. consignment
8. customs
9. duty
10. foreign exchange
11. investment
12. invoice
13. loan
14. progressions
15. promissory note
16. revenue
17. series
18. tariff
19. taxation

Seventh Grade Mathematics Curriculum

The Science of Numbers

Methods

1. Agreeing and disagreeing agreeably
2. Applying Notebook Method: 4-R'ing (researching, reasoning, relating, recording)
3. Comparing
4. Contrasting
5. Conversing with professionals in the field
6. Converting
7. Defining
8. Drawing
9. Engineering
10. Estimating
11. Extending
12. Field study tours
13. Graphing
14. Grouping
15. Journaling
16. Matching
17. Measuring
18. Notating
19. Partitioning
20. Practicing practical problem solving
21. Proving
22. Recognizing visual patterns
23. Reducing
24. Reflecting
25. Sketching
26. Sorting
27. Summarizing
28. Tallying
29. Translating
30. Using a timeline: Math on the Chain of Christianity®
31. Using various tools of mathematicians, i.e., calculators and computers

Resources

Teacher:

1. Bible
2. *Ray's™ New Higher Arithmetic*, Ray, 1985
3. *Mathematics: Is God Silent?*, Nickel, 2001
4. *Men of Mathematics*, Bell, 1965
5. Teacher mathematics notebook
6. Local banks, stock brokers, financial analysts, bookkeepers, tax agencies, economists
7. Computerized software packages related to budgeting, profit & loss statements, balance sheets, computer labs, computerized graphing and probability software.

Student:

1. Bible
2. *Ray's™ New Higher Arithmetic*, Ray, 1985
3. Calculator
4. Computer and CAD software
5. Computerized software packages relating to business transactions
6. Drawing tools
7. Mathematical games and tangram puzzles
8. Student mathematics notebook

Performance Accomplishments

(build on the previous year)

Numbers:

Understands decimals to billionths. Masters percentages with or without the element of time. Proficiently uses the four operations on simple, complex, and compound fractions. Masters reducing fractions, decimals, and percents. Squares, cubes, and extracts the square root or cube root of a number manually or with the aid of a calculating device after mastery. Masterfully solves problems involving compound denominate numbers. Groups numbers into orders through the first twenty-two periods (units through vigintillions). Masters the properties and kinds of numbers, and the principles and rules that relate to them.

Numeration and Notation:

Attains mastery in reading and writing numbers using the Arabic system of notation up to 999 vigintillions. Reads and interprets various scaled data. Constructs geometric shapes manually. Collects and displays data using three-dimensional graphics. Proficiently operates CAD software to solve simple engineering or design problems.

Measurement:

Monetary: Solves producer/consumer problems using U.S. currency and some foreign exchanges. *Linear:* Measures, converts, reduces, and solves practical problems using the English and the metric systems of measurement. *Geometry:* Uses a protractor, sketches three-dimensional shapes, and understands rotational symmetry and graphing. Finds the perimeter and area of a triangle, circle, and a solid. Locates points on a coordinate system. Measures lines, angles, surfaces, and solids. *Time*: Calculates time corresponding to any difference of longitude and longitude corresponding to any difference of time.

Operations:

Addition: Proficiently calculates sums manually with or without decimals and/or with the aid of an abacus, calculator, or computer. Masterfully adds fractions and decimals. Has mastered metrical addition. *Subtraction:* Masterfully subtracts numbers having minuends larger than eleven digits and subtrahends larger than eleven digits, with or without borrowing and with or without decimals, manually or with the aid of a calculating device. *Multiplication*: Masterfully calculates products using factors greater than five digits, with or without decimals, manually in the Arabic or the metric systems. *Division*: Masterfully divides numbers mentally or manually with or without the aid of a computational device. Masterful of aliquots and alligation.

Problem Solving:

Masters manual calculations of squares, square roots, cubes, and cube roots. Solves multi-step story problems making use of a broad range of combinations of addition, subtraction, multiplication, and division using the five-step method to problem solving, applied to measurement, percent, compound denominate numbers, ratio, and proportion. Justifies one's own reasoning using the five-step method to problem solving based upon the principles and rules governing mathematics.

Algebra 1 Mathematics Curriculum
Applied Mathematics

Purposes

1. Reveal God and His divine nature and character through mathematics.
2. Identify and demonstrate the principles governing mathematics.
3. Reason from principles of mathematics and apply them to problem solving.
4. Lay the foundation for virtually all higher mathematics.
5. Introduce probability, data analysis, scatter plots, regression equations, and statistics and their usage.
6. Teach the place of mathematics on the Chain of Christianity® moving westward.
7. Form the character of the American Christian mathematician.

Principles

1. God's Principle of Individuality
2. Principle of representation
3. Commutative principle of addition
4. Associative principle of addition
5. Principle of symmetry
6. Principle of place value

Definitions

1. Mathematics is the science of quantity; of whatever can be measured or numbered. (Webster's 1828 *Dictionary*)
2. Mathematics describes the set of perpetual laws with which God made manifest and upholds the physical universe. It is the expression of His orderly nature that describes the quantitative relationships governing the individual members of creation, from the micro- to the macro-cosmos.
3. Algebra is universal arithmetic. It is a general method of computation in which signs and symbols are made to represent numbers and quantities. It discovers the unknown quantity by means of one or more given quantities to which it is equal.

"For since the creation of the world His invisible attributes, His eternal power and divine nature, have been clearly seen, being understood through what has been made." (Romans 1:20, NASB)

Objectives

1. Attain proficiency in algebraic use of the associative, commutative, and distributive principles.
2. Attain proficiency in algebraic terms, numeration, and notation.
3. Attain proficiency in algebraic thinking and written expression representing something mathematically real.
4. Attain proficiency in finding the value of an expression when the value of x is known and unknown.
5. Relate the following to other subjects in the curriculum:
   - Mathematical applications, careers, and games
   - Engineering tools and projects
   - Computerized graphing software

Foundations

Theme: History of algebra, the universal language of mathematics

Biblical Foundation:

"And He [Jesus] is the radiance of His [God the Father's] glory and the exact representation of His nature, and upholds all things by the word of His power." (Hebrews 1:3)

Math on the Chain of Christianity: History of algebra

1. Mohammed al-Khwarizmi (780–850), "Father of the algorithm"; invented algebra.
2. François Viète (1540–1603), credited with decimals, roots, and co-efficients.
3. George Boole (1815–64), developed Boolean logic.
4. Rudolf Clausius (1822–88), expressed the Second Law of Thermodynamics mathematically.

Vocabulary

1. abstract
2. algebra
3. angle
4. antecedent
5. area
6. axiom
7. base
8. binomial
9. coefficient
10. cubit
11. degree
12. discriminant
13. equation
14. exponent
15. expression
16. factor
17. figure
18. formula
19. identity
20. integer
21. involution
22. monomial
23. numeral
24. polynomial
25. power
26. quadratic
27. radical
28. reciprocal
29. surd
30. theorem
31. transformation
32. transpose
33. trinomial
34. variable

Algebra 1 Mathematics Curriculum
Applied Mathematics

Methods

1. Agreeing and disagreeing agreeably
2. Applying Notebook Method: 4-R'ing (researching, reasoning, relating, recording)
3. Comparing and contrasting
4. Conversing with professionals in the field
5. Converting
6. Defining
7. Drawing
8. Graphing
9. Grouping
10. Measuring
11. Notating
12. Partitioning
13. Practicing practical problem solving
14. Proving
15. Recognizing visual patterns
16. Reducing
17. Summarizing
18. Using tools of mathematics

Resources

Teacher:

1. Bible
2. *Algebra 1: Expressions, Equations, and Applications* (Teacher's Edition), Foerster, 1999
3. *Mathematics: Is God Silent?*, Nickel, 2001
4. *Men of Mathematics*, Bell, 1965
5. Software related to probability and statistics and laboratory graphing

Student:

1. Bible
2. *Algebra 1: Expressions, Equations, and Applications*, Foerster, 1999
3. Calculator and drawing tools

Performance Accomplishments

Numbers:

Substitutes a given value for a variable. Evaluates a given power. Writes a number as a power. Adds, subtracts, multiplies, and divides positive and negative numbers quickly. Determines whether a set of numbers is closed under a certain operation. Factors integers into a product of primes. Multiplies and divides numbers written in scientific notation. Uses long division to divide a lower-degree polynomial into a higher-degree polynomial. Finds the ratio of two numbers in lowest terms. Multiplies and divides binomials containing square roots of constants. Evaluates higher-order radicals. Transforms a repeating decimal into a ratio of integers.

Numeration and Notation:

Attains mastery in reading the Cartesian coordinate system as well as plotting ordered pairs on the system. Transforms numbers into scientific notation. Uses f(x) terminology for the y-value of a function. Writes expressions from a verbal description.

Measurement:

Uses the Pythagorean theorem to calculate the hypotenuse of a right triangle. Uses trigonometric functions to find the length of a side or the measure of an angle.

Operations:

Evaluates, simplifies, transforms, arranges, factors, squares, adds, subtracts, multiplies, and divides rational algebraic expressions. Solves equations with variables in both members. Solves a system of two linear equations with two variables using several methods. Solves and graphs inequalities involving absolute value. Solves and graphs quadratic inequalities.

Problem Solving:

Writes and solves equations representing real-world situations. Given a step in computation, tells which axiom or property justifies that step. Given a formula, evaluates it for various values of the literal constants. Solves problems with two or more variable expressions. Writes and solves problems with two variables and two equations. Given a random experiment, calculates the probability that a certain event will happen. Solves problems using scientific notation. Uses linear functions to predict values of variables, and finds the equation of a linear function that fits scattered data. Graphs inequalities. Given the equation of a function, calculates ordered pairs and then plots its graph.

Algebra 2 Mathematics Curriculum
Applied Mathematics

Purposes

1. Reveal God, His nature, and His character through mathematics.
2. Identify and demonstrate the principles governing mathematics.
3. Reason from principles of mathematics and apply them to problem solving.
4. Teach the place of mathematics on the Chain of Christianity® moving westward.
5. Lay the foundation for virtually all the higher mathematics.
6. Prepare students for a subsequent course in either geometry, trigonometry, or calculus.
7. Introduce probability, data analysis, scatter plots, regression equations, and statistics and their usage.

Principles

1. God's Principle of Individuality
2. Principle of order and magnitude
3. Principle of representation
4. Commutative principle of addition
5. Associative principle of addition
6. Distributive principle
7. Principle of symmetry
8. Principle of the order of operations
9. Equality principle
10. Closure principle
11. Reflexive principle
12. Transitive principle
13. Comparative principle
14. Probability principle
15. Principle of exponents

Definitions

1. Mathematics is the science of quantity or whatever can be measured or numbered. (Webster's 1828 *Dictionary*)
2. Mathematics describes the set of perpetual laws with which God made manifest and upholds the physical universe. It is the expression of His orderly nature that describes the quantitative relationships governing the individual members of creation, from the micro- to the macro-cosmos.
3. Algebra is universal arithmetic. Algebra is a general method of computation in which signs and symbols are made to represent numbers and quantities. It discovers the unknown quantity by means of one or more given quantities to which it is equal.

"For since the creation of the world His invisible attributes, His eternal power and divine nature, have been clearly seen, being understood through what has been made." (Romans 1:20, NASB)

Objectives

(build on algebra 1)

1. Evaluate expressions.
2. Solve and graph equations and inequalities with one variable.
3. Solve linear and quadratic functions.
4. Graph linear and quadratic functions.
5. Find inverses of functions.
6. Solve systems of linear equations.
7. Use calculators in algebraic equations.
8. Proficiently use computer-assisted design (CAD) software.
9. Relate the following to other subjects in the curriculum:
   - Mathematical applications, careers, and games
   - Engineering tools and projects
   - Computerized graphing software

Foundations

Theme: History of algebra, the universal language of mathematics

Biblical Foundation:

"I wisdom dwell with prudence, and find out knowledge of witty inventions. Counsel is mine, and sound wisdom: I am understanding; I have strength." (Proverbs 8:12, 14)

Math on the Chain of Christianity: History of algebra

1. Sir Isaac Newton (1642–1727), wrote *Principia* and developed the Binomial Theorem.
2. Leonhard Euler (1707–83), made decisive and formative contributions to geometry, calculus, and number theory.
3. Leopold Kronecker (1823–91), is noted for the theory of algebraic numbers, the properties of integers, and systems of polynomial equations.
4. Albert Einstein (1879–1955), Theories of Relativity, determined that light is the most fundamental form of energy.

Vocabulary

(build on algebra 1)

1. asymptote
2. combination
3. complex numbers
4. conics
5. constant
6. cosine
7. direct variation
8. domain
9. evaluate
10. function
11. graph
12. imaginary number
13. matrix
14. permutation
15. radian
16. rational number
17. real number
18. sequence
19. series
20. sine
21. slope
22. tangent
23. trigonometric
24. vector

Algebra 2 Mathematics Curriculum
Applied Mathematics

Methods
(build on algebra 1)

1. Determining probability of an event
2. Graphing conic sections
3. Plotting
4. Solving exponential and polynomial functions
5. Synthesizing
6. Transforming
7. Using logarithms to solve exponential equations
8. Using tools of mathematics

Resources

Teacher:

1. Bible
2. *Algebra and Trigonometry: Functions and Applications,* Foerster (Teacher's Edition), 1999
3. *Mathematics: Is God Silent?*, Nickel, 2001
4. *Men of Mathematics,* Bell, 1965
5. Software related to probability and statistics and laboratory graphing

Student:

1. Bible
2. *Algebra and Trigonometry: Functions and Applications,* Foerster, 1999
3. Calculator and drawing tools

Performance Accomplishments
(build on algebra 1)

Numbers:

Classifies real and imaginary numbers; if real, rational and irrational. Recognizes and adds, subtracts, multiplies, and divides complex numbers.

Numeration and Notation:

Attains mastery in reading the Cartesian coordinate system as well as plotting ordered pairs on the system. Transforms numbers into scientific notation. Uses f(x) terminology for the y-value of a function. Writes expressions from a verbal description.

Measurement:

Uses appropriate trigonometric functions to find missing parts of right triangles.

Operations:

Uses matrices to solve systems of equations in two or three variables. Uses synthetic division to determine values of polynomials and determine roots of polynomial equations.

Problem Solving:

Writes and solves equations representing real-world situations. Given a step in computation, tells which axiom or property justifies that step. Given a formula, evaluates it for various values of the literal constants. Solves problems with two or more variable expressions. Writes and solves problems with two variables and two equations. Given a random experiment, calculates the probability that a certain event will happen. Solves problems using scientific notation. Uses linear functions to predict values of variables. Finds the equation of a linear function that fits scattered data. Graphs inequalities. Given the equation of a function, calculates ordered pairs and then plots its graph.

Geometry Mathematics Curriculum
Applied Mathematics

Purposes

1. Reveal God and His divine nature and character through mathematics.
2. Identify and demonstrate the principles governing mathematics.
3. Reason from principles of mathematics and apply them to problem solving.
4. Connect geometry with algebra to real-world applications.
5. Master mathematics as a language as a geometer and encourage deductive reasoning.
6. Introduce probability, data analysis, scatter plots, regression equations, and statistics and their usage.
7. Teach the place of mathematics on the Chain of Christianity® moving westward.
8. Form the character of the American Christian mathematician.

Principles

1. God's Principle of Individuality
2. Principle of representation
3. Principle of substitution
4. Identity principle
5. Inverse principle
6. Closure principle
7. Principle of equalities
8. Principle of inequalities
9. Principle of parallel lines
10. Principle of perpendicular lines

Definitions

1. Mathematics is the science of quantity; of whatever can be measured or numbered. (Webster's 1828 *Dictionary*)
2. Mathematics describes the set of perpetual laws with which God made manifest and upholds the physical universe. It is the expression of His orderly nature that describes the quantitative relationships governing the individual members of creation, from the micro- to the macro-cosmos.
3. Geometry is that branch of mathematics that treats the art of measuring and the science of magnitude.

"For since the creation of the world His invisible attributes, His eternal power and divine nature, have been clearly seen, being understood through what has been made." (Romans 1:20, NASB)

Objectives

(build on algebra)

1. Proficiently apply algebra in geometry.
2. Master the associative, commutative, and distributive principles.
3. Proficiently use geometrical terms and master numeration and notation using geometrical symbols.
4. Attain proficiency in geometric thinking.
5. Proficiently write expressions representing something mathematically real.
6. Understand how to apply geometry to a variety of occupational and career goals.
7. Proficiently use computer-assisted design (CAD) software.
8. Relate the following to other subjects in the curriculum:
   - Mathematical applications, careers, and games
   - Engineering tools and projects
   - Computerized graphing software

Foundations

Theme: History of geometry

Biblical Foundation:

"Where were you when I laid the foundation of the earth? Tell Me, if you have understanding, who set its measurements? Since you know. Or who stretched the line on it? On what were its bases sunk? Or who laid its cornerstone?" (Job 38:4–6)

Math on the Chain of Christianity: History of geometry

1. Euclid (330–275 B.C.), greatest mathematician of antiquity; wrote *Elements*, next to the Bible, the most influential book.
2. Bonaventura Cavalieri (1598–1647), Cavalieri theorem; conic sections; contributed to trigonometry.
3. Pierre de Fermat (1601?–65), measured the earth; most noted for his work on number theory, Fermat's Last Theorem
4. Jean Poncelet (1788–1867), developed the pole and polar lines associated with conics, which led to the principle of duality.

Vocabulary

(build on algebra)

1. adjacent
2. apothem
3. arc
4. axiom
5. bisect
6. chord
7. circumscribe
8. coincident
9. collinear
10. complement
11. concave
12. congruent
13. contrapositive
14. convex
15. corollary
16. cosine
17. hypotenuse
18. hypothesis
19. inequality
20. inscribe
21. intercept
22. isosceles
23. locus
24. magnitude
25. midpoint
26. obtuse
27. postulate
28. proof
29. ray
30. scalene
31. sector
32. segment
33. supplement
34. tangent
35. theorem

Geometry Mathematics Curriculum
Applied Mathematics

Methods

(build on algebra)

1. Agreeing and disagreeing agreeably
2. Applying Notebook Method: 4-R'ing (researching, reasoning, relating, recording)
3. Constructing
4. Explaining
5. Extending
6. Graphing
7. Measuring
8. Modeling
9. Notating
10. Paper folding and cutting
11. Plotting
12. Proving
13. Recognizing visual patterns
14. Sketching
15. Strategizing
16. Summarizing
17. Synthesizing
18. Transforming
19. Using tools of mathematics

Resources

Teacher:

1. Bible
2. *Geometry: Applying, Reasoning, Measuring* (Teacher's Edition), Larson, Boswell, and Stiff, 2001
3. *Mathematics: Is God Silent?*, Nickel, 2001
4. *Men of Mathematics*, Bell, 1965
5. Geo-boards
6. Teacher mathematics notebook
7. Software related to geometric problem solving and laboratory graphing

Student:

1. Bible
2. *Geometry: Applying, Reasoning, Measuring*, Larson, Boswell, and Stiff, 2001
3. Computer and software packages relating to engineering, architecture, and business transactions
4. Geometrical games and tangram puzzles
5. Student mathematics notebook

Performance Accomplishments

(build on algebra)

Numeration and Notation:

Proficiently reads and writes numbers and geometric expressions using the Arabic system of notation and the following symbols: $|x|$, $\approx$, $\neq$, $\leq$ $\geq$, $>$, $<$, $f(x)$, π, $\sqrt{\ }$, $\sqrt[3]{\ }$, (x, y), (x, y, z), a:b, a/b, cos A, sin A, tan A, $\|$, °. Writes and simplifies the ratio of two numbers.

Measurement:

Identifies and accurately measures objects, lines, perimeters, angles, and areas of various geometric shapes. Uses a straightedge and a compass to make basic constructions. Understands the structure of geometry (terms, postulates, and theorems).

Problem Solving:

Uses vector operations, the laws of logic, special segments, and inequalities to prove theorems and/or solve problems with practical applications.

Precalculus Mathematics Curriculum
Applied Mathematics

Purposes

1. Reveal God and His divine nature and character through mathematics.
2. Identify and demonstrate the principles governing mathematics.
3. Reason from principles of mathematics and apply them to problem solving.
4. Identify and demonstrate the principles governing mathematics and higher order algebraic manipulations, functions, and trigonometry.
5. Understand the principle of functions and how it relates to mathematical models of physical world actions and reactions.
6. Master mathematics as the fundamental language upon which science and technology are based.
7. Teach the place of mathematics on the Chain of Christianity® moving westward.
8. Form the character of the American Christian mathematician.

Principles

1. God's Principle of Individuality
2. Principle of representation
3. Commutative principle of addition
4. Associative principle of addition
5. Principle of symmetry
6. Principle of place value

Definitions

1. Mathematics is the science of quantity; of whatever can be measured or numbered. (Webster's 1828 *Dictionary*)
2. Mathematics describes the set of perpetual laws with which God made manifest and upholds the physical universe. It is the expression of His orderly nature that describes the quantitative relationships governing the individual members of creation, from the micro- to the macro-cosmos.
3. Analytical geometry is resolving problems by geometry using algebraic equations.
4. Trigonometry is the measuring of triangles; the science of determining the sides and angles of triangles, by means of certain parts which are given.
5. Calculus is that branch of mathematics that treats the differencing of variable, exponential, and differential quantities.

"For since the creation of the world His invisible attributes, His eternal power and divine nature, have been clearly seen, being understood through what has been made." (Romans 1:20, NASB)

Objectives

(build on algebra and geometry)

1. Master algebraic manipulations in solving equations, inequalities, and systems of both.
2. Master graphing of linear, polynomial, exponential, logarithmic, and trigonometric functions.
3. Attain proficiency in employing complex and imaginary numbers in solutions.
4. Attain proficiency in employing logarithmic properties in problem solving.
5. Master trigonometric functions and their application in problem solving.
6. Attain proficiency in employing matrices and their application in problem solving.
7. Attain proficiency in employment of probability and statistics for analysis of data and problem solving.
8. Master manipulation of conic section functions and their graphs.
9. Attain proficiency in employing vector analysis toward problem solving in physical sciences and engineering applications.
10. Relate the following to other subjects in the curriculum:
    - Mathematical applications, careers, and games
    - Engineering tools and projects
    - Computerized graphing software

Foundations

Theme: History of trigonometry and calculus

Biblical Foundation:

"For the word of the LORD is right; and all his works are done in truth. By the word of the LORD were the heavens made; and all the host of them by the breath of his mouth." (Psalm 33:4, 6)

Math on the Chain of Christianity: History of the science of numbers

1. Evangelista Torricelli (1608–47), the area and tangent of cycloid.
2. Blaise Pascal (1623–62), invented first digital calculator; wrote *Pensees;* is best known for Pascal Triangle and his work on binomial coefficients.
3. René Descartes (1596–1650), developed analytic geometry and the Cartesian coordinate system.
4. George William Hill (1838–1914), developed the Theory of Linear Differential Equations with Periodic Coefficients.

Vocabulary

(build on algebra and geometry)

1. asymptotes
2. composite functions
3. conic section
4. conjugate
5. continuity
6. cosecant
7. cotangent
8. dispersion
9. domain
10. exponential
11. factorial
12. focus
13. functions
14. imaginary number
15. inverse functions
16. limits
17. logarithm
18. matrix, matrices
19. median
20. mode
21. permutation
22. polar
23. probability
24. range
25. radian
26. scatter
27. series
28. sine
29. standard deviation
30. statistics
31. variation
32. vector
33. vertex, vertices

Precalculus Mathematics Curriculum
Applied Mathematics

Methods

1. Agreeing and disagreeing agreeably
2. Applying Notebook Method: 4-R'ing (researching, reasoning, relating, recording)
3. Comparing and contrasting
4. Converting
5. Defining
6. Drawing
7. Estimating
8. Extending
9. Graphing
10. Grouping
11. Measuring
12. Notating
13. Partitioning
14. Practicing practical problem solving
15. Proving
16. Recognizing visual patterns
17. Reducing
18. Reflecting
19. Summarizing
20. Translating
21. Using tools of mathematics

Resources

Teacher:

1. Bible
2. *Precalculus with Limits: A Graphing Approach*, 3rd Ed. (Instructor's Annotated Edition). Larson, Hostetler, and Edwards, 2001
3. *Mathematics: Is God Silent?*, Nickel, 2001
4. *Men of Mathematics*, Bell, 1965
5. Teacher mathematics notebook
6. Graphing calculator with overhead projector adapter
7. Software related to probability and statistics and laboratory graphing

Student:

1. Bible
2. *Precalculus with Limits: A Graphing Approach*, 3rd Ed. Larson, Hostetler, Edwards, 2001
3. *Study and Solutions Guide [for Precalculus with Limits: A Graphing Approach]* (Student's Edition). Larson, Hostetler, and Edwards, 2001
4. Graphing calculator, instruction manual, and workbook
5. Computer and software (visualization of concepts)
6. Student mathematics notebook

Performance Accomplishments

Numeration and Notation:

Reads and writes with proficiency numbers and algebraic expressions using the Arabic system of notation and the following symbols: cosine, sine, tangent, cotangent, secant, cosecant, arccos, arcsine, arctan, arccot, arcsec, arccsc, $\cos^{-1}$, $\sin^{-1}$, $\tan^{-1}$, $\sec^{-1}$, $\csc^{-1}$, $f(x)$, $f^{-1}(x)$, $f \circ g$, $f(g(x))$, log, ln, e, rad, i, $a + bi$, [ ], det (A), n!, Σ, σ, nPm, nCm.

Measurement:

Identifies, graphs, and manipulates functions, their inverses, and their characteristic behavior algebraically for solutions. Identifies mathematical models requiring employment of a system of equations and inequalities. Recognizes statistical analysis scenarios requiring measures of central tendency and measures of dispersion.

Problem Solving:

Solves various functions for application in the sciences and technology manually and with graphing calculator. Derives solutions through matrices, inverses, probability, series, sequences, and permutations. Statistically analyzes data through measures of central tendency and dispersion.

Calculus Mathematics Curriculum
Applied Mathematics

Purposes

1. Reveal God and His divine nature and character through mathematics.
2. Identify and demonstrate the principles governing mathematics and higher order algebraic manipulations, functions, trigonometry, derivatives, and integrals.
3. Reason from principles of mathematics and apply them to the sciences and real-world problem solving.
4. Master mathematics as the fundamental language upon which science and technology are based.
5. Teach the place of mathematics on the Chain of Christianity® moving westward.
6. Form the character of the American Christian mathematician.

Principles

1. God's Principle of Individuality
2. Principle of representation
3. Equality principle
4. Principle of limits
5. Principle of asymptotes and unbounded behavior
6. Principle of continuity
7. Principles of technological graphing
8. Principles of derivatives and instantaneous rate of change on a curve
9. Principles of tangent and normal lines to a curve
10. Principles of graphs of functions and the 1st and 2nd derivatives
11. Principles of the mean value theorem
12. Principles of concavity and inflection
13. Principles of optimization
14. Principles of L'Hôpital's rule
15. Principles of integration
16. Principle of the fundamental theorem of calculus
17. Principle of Riemann sums and the trapezoidal rule

Definitions

1. Mathematics is the science of quantity; of whatever can be measured or numbered. (Webster's 1828 *Dictionary*)
2. Mathematics describes the set of perpetual laws with which God made manifest and upholds the physical universe. It is the expression of His orderly nature that describes the quantitative relationships governing the individual members of creation, from the micro- to the macro-cosmos.
3. Calculus is that branch of mathematics that treats the differencing of variable, exponential, and differential quantities.

"For since the creation of the world His invisible attributes, His eternal power and divine nature, have been clearly seen, being understood through what has been made." (Romans 1:20, NASB)

Objectives

(build on precalculus)

1. Master manipulation of functions algebraically, graphically, analytically, and verbally.
2. Master translation of the spoken word into mathematical expressions.
3. Master the concept of a derivative in terms of rate of change.
4. Master the concept of definite integrals both as a limit of Riemann sums and as the net accumulation of rate of change.
5. Master the relationships between derivatives and integrals in the Fundamental Theorem of Calculus.
6. Master communication in mathematics: orally, written sentences, and notationally.
7. Master modeling a written description of a physical situation with a function, differential equation, or an integral.
8. Master the employment of technology in the solution of problems, demonstrating concepts, and communication of mathematics.
9. Relate the following to other subjects in the curriculum:
   - Mathematical applications, careers, and games
   - Engineering tools and projects
   - Computerized graphing software

Foundations

Theme: History of calculus

Biblical Foundation:

"My mouth shall tell of Your righteousness and Your salvation all the day for I do not know their limits." (Psalm 71:15, NKJV)

Math on the Chain of Christianity: History of calculus

1. Nicolaus Copernicus (1473–1543), initiated the scientific revolution; the geo-heliocentric theory.
2. Johannes Kepler (1571–1630), developed the Principle of Continuity.
3. Gottfried Liebnitz (1646–1716) furthered the development of integral calculus.
4. Karl Gauss (1777–1855), "prince of mathematicians," applied calculus to geometry.

Vocabulary

(build on precalculus)

1. chain rule
2. concavity
3. continuity
4. derivative
5. implicit differentiation
6. inflection
7. limits
8. optimization
9. Riemann sums

Calculus Mathematics Curriculum
Applied Mathematics

Methods

1. Agreeing and disagreeing agreeably
2. Analyzing
3. Applying Notebook Method: 4-R'ing (researching, reasoning, relating, recording)
4. Comparing and contrasting
5. Converting
6. Defining
7. Drawing
8. Estimating
9. Extending
10. Graphing
11. Measuring
12. Modeling
13. Notating
14. Partitioning
15. Practicing practical problem solving
16. Proving
17. Summarizing
18. Synthesizing
19. Using tools of mathematics

Resources

Teacher:

1. Bible
2. *Calculus with Analytic Geometry* 6th Ed., Chap. P–15 (Instructor's Resource Guide, Chapters P–15), Larson, Hostetler, Edwards, 1998
3. Instructor's *Complete Solutions Guide to Accompany Calculus Sixth Edition*, Larson, Vol. 1, Preface–5 & Vol. 2 6–9 (single variable), Vol. 3, 10–15 (multivariable)
4. *Mathematics: Is God Silent?*, Nickel, 2001
5. *Men of Mathematics*, Bell, 1965
6. Teacher mathematics notebook
7. Graphing calculator with overhead projector adapter
8. Software related to probability and statistics and laboratory graphing

Student:

1. Bible
2. *Calculus with Analytic Geometry* 6th Ed., Larson, Hostetler, Edwards, 1998
3. Student's Edition, *Complete Solutions Guide to Accompany Calculus*, 6th Ed., Larson. Preface–9 (single variable), & 10–15 (multivariable)
4. Graphing calculator, instruction manual, and workbook
5. Computer and software (visualization of concepts)
6. Student mathematics notebook

Performance Accomplishments

Numeration and Notation:

Attains mastery in reading and writing numbers and algebraic expressions using the Arabic system of notation and the following symbols: lim, $f'(x)$, $f''(x)$, d/dx, dy/dx, d^2y/dx^2, $\int x dx$ $\iint$, $\iiint$ axis intercepts, and their unbounded behavior.

Measurement:

Identifies properties of limits of functions. States the definition of and graphically interprets continuity and discontinuity. Finds the derivative of algebraic functions. States the Mean Value Theorem and applies it both graphically and algebraically. Applies Newton's method of estimating zeros.

Problem Solving:

Identifies continuous and discontinuous functions and solves for limits of functions. Identifies the properties of the Fundamental Theorem of Calculus and applies it to scientific and technological problems using optimization techniques.

Chapter Two

Foundations: An American Christian Philosophy of Mathematics

Beware lest anyone cheat you through philosophy
and empty deceit, according to the tradition of men,
according to the basic principles of the world,
and not according to Christ.
(Colossians 2:8, NKJV)

PRINCIPLE APPROACH® EDUCATION
SPIRIT OF CHRIST
Methodology
Philosophy
Results
Curriculum

Notes

Introducing an American Christian Philosophy of Mathematics

Philosophy is written in that great book (nature) which ever lies before our eyes—but we cannot understand it if we do not first learn the language and grasp the symbols in which it is written. The book is written in the mathematical language, and the symbols are triangles, circles and other geometrical figures, without whose help it is impossible to comprehend a single word of it, without which one wanders in vain through a dark labyrinth.

(Galileo Galilei, 1623)

A Christian philosophy of mathematics gives rise to a Christian curriculum and a distinctly Christian methodology. Research in the changes that have occurred in mathematics curricula over the last century indicates that the pendulum has swung from a Christian worldview to a secular one, from having a master teacher instruct through problem solving and drill to the incidental, experiential approach wherein students must try to learn from self-led experiments. Today, American students score lowest in math and science when tested with the world's top forty-one industrialized nations. Why is it that believers continue to submit to the world's educational system and mediocre curriculum? In a world of debased values and third-rate education, it is time for the standard of Truth to be raised in Christian education. There should be no dichotomy between the sacred and secular for the thinking Christian!

An individual's worldview determines his view of mathematics. A math curriculum that is governed by a Biblical, Christian philosophy of education forms a Biblical, Christian world- and life view in students. It emphasizes mathematical thinking, logical reasoning, and problem solving based upon the authority of God's inspired, living Word and the Biblical principles that reveal His universe as well as the governing principles within the discipline. The methodology helps students internalize truth, not just recall facts to pass the test. It cultivates mastery of mathematical precepts within students and requires the application of reasoning to problem solving. The internalization of principles through Christian methods enables students to interpret information using symbolic statements in terms of appropriate mental models, to analyze them, and to understand the precepts. It does not consist of a large number of routine mathematical procedures superficially learned and rarely understood or of asking students to experiment with the principle and arrive at their own conclusions. It verifies God as the Great Mathematician.

A Biblical, Christian worldview holds that mathematics was used by God when He created the physical universe and its immutable laws reveal the attributes of His nature and character. When studied with the revelation of His Word, mathematics is an expression of God's reasoning written in symbols by man. Mathematics is thinking analytically about specific types of quantities that originate in God and with God. Understanding the principles of mathematics and the purposeful reasoning about quantities lays the foundation for applying the laws of His handiwork to all the sciences and technology. Mathematics, when studied in the light of God's Word, is an essential tool for man in fulfilling God's command to take dominion over all the earth. (Genesis 1:28)

Laying a Biblical Foundation for Teaching Mathematics

For no man can lay a foundation other than the one which is laid, which is Jesus Christ.
(1 Corinthians 3:11, NASB)

Mathematics is the language with which God fashioned His creation. "In the beginning was the Word, and the Word was with God, and the Word was God. He was in the beginning with God. All

Notes

To teach the mechanics of mathematics without introducing students to the Great Mathematician is to rob the life and energy from it.

things came into being through Him, and apart from Him nothing came into being that has come into being." (John 1:1–3, NASB) God spoke; the heavens and earth came into existence (Genesis 1) and are upheld by the word of His power. (Hebrews 1:3)

Language and ideas have played a crucial role in the interaction between God the Creator and His creation. The stars in the sky, the countless galaxies spinning through physical space, the atoms that make up our physical bodies, all of these were made manifest by God's Word. The patterns of God's speech laid the structure of the whole universe and logically describe for us the immutable laws of His handiwork.

The sciences are man's inquiries into the nature, mystery, and majesty of God's creation, so that we may learn more of His nature by studying His handiwork. Inquiry into the principles of mathematics allows us a rare, yet discernable, glimpse of the full perfection and divine genius of God. The laws of mathematics are completely pure and incorruptible. Unlike man-made laws or theories, they cannot be broken, bent, or found false. And yet, even the simplest of mathematical principles can be seen at work in the greatest mysteries of the universe. Galileo Galilei called the physical universe the great "book of nature" and believed that it was written in the language of mathematics. To him the laws of nature brought clear testimony of a Lawgiver.

Mathematics is not just about boring numbers and staid equations. Rather, it is about the form of expression that God deemed suitable for completely and logically describing His physical creation! Take for example the Fibonacci numbers and Golden Ratio (*phi*), described in the thirteenth century by Leonardo of Pisa. Today, even secular philosophers and scientists ascribe awe and wonder to the elegant spiral growth patterns found in pinecones, sunflower seed heads, and nautilus shells, as they describe them with the logarithmic spiral. Some formulas and equations are so complex, like fractal equations, that each equation in itself contains a look at an infinite amount of diversity; such things only serve to illustrate the vast power and divine origin of the language of mathematics!

"As a disciplined thought structure, mathematics describes both the numerical and spatial aspects of God's creational structure that enable man to explore the vast wonders of His creation."[1] There are stunning revelations of the diversity of God behind those mysterious mathematical formulas, which, for man, are the keys that unlock the fundamental nature and design of the physical universe. Through the unveiling of these mysteries, man comes to know God as both a personal, loving Heavenly Father and the Creator and Sovereign Ruler of all!

Both teacher and student must know the living God of the Bible as the Creator and Sovereign Ruler of the universe through a personal relationship with His Son, Jesus Christ, whose authoritative Word holds the power and life for all pursuits of knowledge and understanding. To teach the mechanics of mathematics without introducing students to the Great Mathematician is to rob the life and energy from it.

As Christians, we have permitted secular mathematicians to instruct us with their godless philosophy of education and to write our math curriculum. They taught us that "God is silent in mathematics, and we believed them."[2] *The Noah Plan® Mathematics Curriculum Guide* seeks to point out the voice of God in teaching and learning mathematics through the Principle Approach®, "America's historic method of reasoning that places the truths of God's Word at the heart of each subject."[3]

Elizabeth L. Youmans, ED.D.

---

1 James Nickel, *Mathematics: Is God Silent?* expanded edition. Vallecito, CA: Ross House Books, 2001, 83.

2 Larry Zimmerman, "Mathematics: Is God Silent? Part II," *The Biblical Educator*, Vol. II, No. 2. Sterling, VA: Institute for Christian Economics, 1980.

3 Rosalie J. Slater, *Teaching and Learning America's Christian History: The Principle Approach.* Foundation for American Christian Education, 1965, 52.

Defining the Vocabulary of Mathematics

Notes

mathematics, *n.* [L. *mathematica*, from Gr. to learn] (key words bolded and defined below)

1. The ***science*** of **quantity**; the science which treats of **magnitude** and **number**, or of whatever can be **measured** or numbered. This science is divided into **pure** or **speculative**, which considers quantity abstractly, without relation to matter; and mixed, which treats of magnitude as subsisting in material bodies, and is consequently interwoven with physical considerations. It is the **peculiar excellence** of *mathematics*, that its **principles** are **demonstrable. Arithmetic, geometry, algebra, trigonometry,** and **conic sections,** are branches of *mathematics*. (Webster's 1828 *Dictionary*)
2. The language of God expressed in creation, the patterns of which laid the structure of the universe and describe the laws of His handiwork. (Editor)
3. Mathematics describes the set of perpetual laws with which God made manifest and upholds the physical universe. It is the expression of His orderly nature that describes the quantitative relationships governing the individual members of creation, from the micro- to the macrocosmos. (Hebrews 1:3; Colossians 1:17) (Editor)
4. An entity which perhaps always exists in the mind of God, and which is for man the universal expression of His creative and sustaining word of power. (Larry Zimmerman)[1]

Key Words from Webster's 1828 *Dictionary*

science, *n.* [Fr. from L. *scientia*, from *scio*, to know; Sp. *ciencia*; It. *scienza*. *Scio* is probably a contracted word.] (1) In *a general sense*, knowledge, or certain knowledge; the comprehension or understanding of truth or facts by the mind. The *science* of God must be perfect. (2) In *philosophy*, a collection of the general principles or leading truths relating to any subject. *Pure* science, as the mathematics, is built on self-evident truths; but the term science is also applied to other subjects founded on generally acknowledged truths, as *metaphysics*; or on experiment and observation, as *chimistry* [sic] and *natural philosophy*; or even to an assemblage of the general principles of an art, as the science of *agriculture*; the science of *navigation*. *Arts* relate to practice, as painting and sculpture.

quantity, *n.* [Fr. *quantité*; It. *quantità*; Sp. *cantitad*; from L. *quantitas*, from *quantus*, how much, or as much as; . . .] In *mathematics*, any thing which can be multiplied, divided or measured. Thus mathematics is called the science of quantity. In algebra, quantities are *known* and *unknown*. *Known quantities* are usually represented by the first letters of the alphabet, as *a*, *b*, *c*, and *unknown quantities* are expressed by the last letters, *x*, *y*, *z*, &c. Letters thus used to represent quantities are themselves called quantities. A simple quantity is expressed by one term, as $+a$, or $-abc$; a compound is expressed by more terms than one, connected by the signs, + plus, or – minus, as $a + b$, or $a - b + c$. Quantities which have the sign + prefixed, are called *positive* or *affirmative*; those which have the sign - prefixed are called *negative*.

magnitude, *n.* [L. *magnitudo*.] Extent of dimensions or parts; bulk; size; *applied to things that have length, breadth or thickness.*

number, *n.* [Fr. *nombre*; L. *numerus*; It. Sp. Port. *numero*; Arm. W. *niver*; Ir. *nuimhir*. . . . the radical sense is to speak, name or tell, as our word *tell*, in the other dialects, is to number. *Number* may be allied to *name*, as the Spaniards use *nombre* for name, and the French word written with the same letters, is *number*. . . .] (1) The designation of a unit in reference to other units, or in reckoning, counting, enumerating; as, one is the first *number*; a simple *number*. (2) An assemblage of two or more units. Two is a

---

[1] Larry Zimmerman, "Mathematics: Is God Silent? Part II," *The Biblical Educator*, Vol. II, No. 2. Sterling, VA: Institute for Christian Economics, 1980.

Notes

number composed of one and one added. Five and three added make the *number* eight. *Number* may be applied to any collection or multitude of units or individuals, and therefore is indefinite, unless defined by other words or by figures or signs of definite signification. (3) In *mathematics*, number is variously distinguished. *Cardinal numbers* are those which express the amount of units; as 1. 2. 3. 4. 5. 6. 7. 8. 9. 10. *Ordinal numbers* are those which express order; as first, second, third, fourth, etc. *Determinate number*, is that referred to a given unit, as a ternary or three; an *indeterminate number*, is referred to unity in general, and called quantity. *Homogeneal numbers*, are those referred to the same units; those referred to different units are termed *heterogeneal*. *Whole numbers*, are called *integers*. A *rational number*, is one commensurable with unity. A number incommensurable with unity, is termed *irrational* or *surd*. A *prime* or *primitive number*, is divisible only by unity; as three, five, seven, etc. A *perfect number*, is that whose aliquot parts added together, make the whole number, as 28, whose aliquot parts, 14. 7. 4. 2. 1. make the number 28. An *imperfect number*, is that whose aliquot parts added together, make more or less than the number. This is abundant or defective; abundant, as 12, whose aliquot parts, 6. 4. 3. 2. 1. make 16; or defective, as 16, whose aliquot parts, 8. 4. 2. 1. make 15 only. A *square number*, is the product of a number multiplied by itself; as, 16 is the square number of 4. A *cubic number*, is the product of a square number by its root; as, 27 is the product of the square number 9 by its root 3. *Golden number*, the cycle of the moon, or revolution of 19 years, in which time the conjunctions, oppositions and other aspects of the moon are nearly the same as they were on the same days of the month 19 years before.

measure, *n*. [Fr. *mesure*; . . . G. *mass*, measure; . . . L. . . . *mensura* from *mensus*, . . . to measure, Eng. to *mete*; . . . The sense is to come to, to fall, to happen, and this sense is connected with that of stretching, extending, . . .] (1) The whole extent or dimensions of a thing, including length, breadth and thickness. The *measure* thereof is longer than the earth and broader than the sea. Job xi. (2) That by which extent or dimension is ascertained, either length, breadth, thickness, capacity, or amount; as, a rod or pole is a *measure* of five yards and a half; an inch, a foot, a yard, are *measures* of length; a gallon is a *measure* of capacity. Weights and *measures* should be uniform. Silver and gold are the common *measure* of value. (3) In *geometry*, any quantity assumed as one or unity, to which the ratio of other homogeneous or similar quantities is expressed.

pure, *a*. [L. *purus*; . . . Heb. בר The verb ברר signifies to separate, free, clear; . . .] (1) Unmixed; separate from any other subject or from every thing foreign; as *pure* mathematics.

speculative, *a*. [Fr. *speculatif*; It. *speculativo*.] (1) Given to speculation; contemplative; *applied to persons*. (2) Formed by speculation; theoretical; idea; not verified by fact, experiment or practice; as a scheme merely *speculative*.

peculiar, *a*. [L. *peculiaris*, from *peculium*, one's own property, from *pecus*, cattle.] (1) Appropriate; belonging to a person and to him only. Almost every writer has a *peculiar* style. Most men have manners *peculiar* to themselves. (2) Singular; particular. The man has something *peculiar* in his deportment. (3) Particular; special.

excellence, *n*. [Fr. from L. *excellentia*.] (1) The state of possessing good qualities in an unusual or eminent degree; the state of excelling in any thing. (2) Any valuable quality; any thing highly laudable, meritorious or virtuous, in persons, or valuable and esteemed, in things.

principle, *n*. [. . . L. *principium*, beginning.] (1) In a *general sense*, the cause, source or origin of any thing; that from which a thing proceeds; as the *principle* of motion; the *principles* of action. (2) Element; constituent part; primordial substance. (3) Being that produces any thing; operative cause. (4) In *science*, a truth admitted either without proof, or considered as having been before proved. In the former sense, it is synonymous with *axiom*; in the latter, with the phrase, *established principle*.

Notes

demonstrable, *a*. That may be demonstrated; that may be proved beyond doubt or contradiction; capable of being shown by certain evidence, or by evidence that admits of no doubt; as, the principles of geometry are *demonstrable*.

arithmetic, *n*. [Gr. to number, the art of numbering, from number; . . . rhythm, order, agreement.]

The science of numbers, or the art of computation. The various operations of arithmetic are performed by addition, subtraction, multiplication and division.

geometry, *n*. [Gr. the earth, and measure.] Originally and properly, the art of measuring the earth, or any distances or dimensions on it. But geometry now denotes the science of magnitude in general, comprehending the doctrine and relations of whatever is susceptible of augmentation and diminution; as the mensuration of lines, surfaces, solids, velocity, weight, etc. with their various relations.

algebra, *n*. [. . . The reduction of parts to a whole, or fractions to whole numbers, from the verb, which signifies to consolidate; . . .] The science of quantity in general, or universal arithmetic. Algebra is a general method of computation, in which signs and symbols, which are commonly the letters of the alphabet, are made to represent numbers and quantities. It takes an unknown quantity sought, as if granted; and, by means of one or more quantities given, proceeds till the quantity supposed is discovered, by some other known quantity to which it is equal. This science was of Oriental discovery; but whether among the Arabians or Indians, is uncertain.

trigonometry, *n*. [Gr. a triangle, and, to measure.] The measuring of triangles; the science of determining the sides and angles of triangles, by means of certain parts which are given. When this science is applied to the solution of plane triangles, it is called *plane* trigonometry; when its application is to spherical triangles, it is called *spherical* trigonometry.

conic sections, conics, *n*. That part of geometry which treats of the cone and the curves which arise from its sections. A curve line formed by the intersection of a cone and plane. The conic sections are the parabola, hyperbola, and ellipsis.

Notes

Biblical Principles of a Christian Philosophy of Mathematics

> This year my math teacher taught me in every lesson how God fits into math and how math fits into life. Without God, man would not exist. Without God, man, and math, construction would not exist. The list goes on and on. You can see that my teacher has helped me to have many career choices. When I came to StoneBridge, I was already successful in math. What my teacher helped me do is see what math really is. It's not just numbers and symbols. It's a gift of knowledge from God to man.
>
> Zachary P.
> Sixth Grade,
> StoneBridge School
> Chesapeake, Virginia

1. God is eternal and self-existent.

   "And God said unto Moses, I AM THAT I AM." (Exodus 3:14)

   "But the LORD is the true God, he is the living God, and an everlasting king." (Jeremiah 10:10)

2. God (the Trinity) created the heaven and the earth.

   "In the beginning God created the heaven and the earth." (Genesis 1:1)

   "He [Christ] is the image of the invisible God, the firstborn of all creation. For by Him all things were created, both in the heavens and on earth, visible and invisible, whether thrones or dominions or rulers or authorities—all things have been created by Him and for Him. He is before all things, and in Him all things hold together." (Colossians 1:15–17, NASB)

3. Jesus Christ is the essential, eternal Word, who was Himself before all time and all worlds.

   "In the beginning was the Word, and the Word was with God, and the Word was God. The same was in the beginning with God. All things were made by him; and without him was not any thing made that was made." (John 1:1–3)

   "I am Alpha and Omega, the beginning and the ending, saith the Lord, which is, and which was, and which is to come, the Almighty." (Revelation 1:8)

4. In the beginning, the triune God spoke, and by the power of His Word, the universe came into existence.

   "In the beginning God created the heaven and the earth. And the earth was without form and void; and darkness was upon the face of the deep. And the spirit of God moved upon the face of the waters. And God said, Let there be light: and there was light." (Genesis 1:1–3)

   "By the word of the LORD the heavens were made, and by the breath of His mouth all their host. . . . For He spoke, and it was done; He commanded, and it stood fast." (Psalm 33:6, 9, NASB)

   "Great is our Lord and abundant in strength; His understanding is infinite." (Psalm 147:5, NASB)

5. The study of mathematics unlocks the nature of the physical world.

   "[B]ecause that which is known about God is evident within them; for God made it evident to them. For since the creation of the world His invisible attributes, His eternal power and divine nature, have been clearly seen, being understood through what has been made, so that they are without excuse." (Romans 1:19–20, NASB)

6. The study of mathematics reveals the attributes of God's divine nature and character, and leads man to the knowledge of the living God.

   "For since the creation of the world His invisible attributes, His eternal power and divine nature, have been clearly seen, being understood through what has been made, so that they are without excuse." (Romans 1:20, NASB)

   a. God is spirit (An immaterial intelligent being).

      "God is a Spirit." (John 4:24)
      "the Spirit of truth." (John 14:17)

      "God is a Spirit, in and of himself infinite in being, glory, blessedness, and perfection; all-sufficient, eternal, unchangeable, incomprehensible, everywhere present, almighty, knowing all things, most wise, most holy, most just, most merciful and gracious, long-suffering, and abundant in goodness and truth." (Answer to Question 7 in the Westminster Larger Catechism)

   b. God is self-existent (exists by its own nature or essence, independent of any other cause. God is the only self-existent being).

      "Jesus said to them, 'Truly, truly, I say to you, before Abraham was born, I am.'" (John 8:58, NASB)

Notes

c. God is eternal (without beginning or end of existence).

"Before the mountains were born, Or You gave birth to the earth and the world, Even from everlasting to everlasting, You are God." (Psalm 90:2, NASB)

"The eternal God is a dwelling place, And underneath are the everlasting arms." (Deuteronomy 33:27a-b, NASB)

d. God is infinite (unlimited extent of time, space, or quantity; boundless), and his perfections (complete possession of all moral excellence) are infinite.

"Great is our Lord, and abundant in strength; His understanding is infinite." (Psalm 147:5, NASB)

e. God is perfect (complete; finished; consummate; not defective; complete in moral excellencies).

"Therefore you are to be perfect, as your heavenly Father is perfect." (Matthew 5:48, NASB)

f. God is omnipresent (present in all places at the same time, an attribute peculiar to God).

"one God and Father of all who is over all and through all and in all." (Ephesians 4:6, NASB)

g. God is omniscient (having universal knowledge; infinitely knowing all things at once; all-seeing).

"For whom he did foreknow, he also did predestinate to be conformed to the image of his Son, that he might be the firstborn among many brethren." (Romans 8:29)

"Great is our Lord, and of great power; his understanding is infinite." (Psalm 147:5)

h. God is constant (fixed; not varied; unchanged; permanent) and immutable (the quality that renders change or alteration impossible).

"For I, the LORD, do not change; therefore you, O sons of Jacob, are not consumed." (Malachi 3:6, NASB)

"Jesus Christ the same yesterday, and to day, and for ever." (Hebrews 13:8)

Mathematics, as an expression of God's nature and character, is unchangeable. 1+1+1=3 is just as true today as it was before the foundation of the earth when the triune God existed as God the Father, God the Son, and God the Holy Spirit, three-in-one. Mathematics and its principles are immutable because God is unchangeable!

i. God is orderly (according to an established method) and systematic (having a regular method or order forming a unified whole).

"Let all things be done decently and in order." (1 Corinthians 14:40)

Mathematics, as an expression of God's nature and character, is orderly. The orderly arrangement of numbers, mathematical symbols, and operations are required to calculate the one correct answer else an erroneous answer is obtained. When one violates the order of operations in an algebraic equation an erroneous calculation results. Mathematics is orderly because God is!

Mathematics is governed by principles, laws, and rules and, therefore, is dependable. If the language of mathematics lacked a systematic set of principles, it would reliably result in chaos. Mathematics is systematic because God is systematic!

j. God is exact, accurate, and precise (in exact conformity to truth, or a standard or rule, or to a model; free from failure, error, or defect).

"For verily I say unto you, Till heaven and earth pass, one jot or one tittle shall in no wise pass from the law, till all be fulfilled." (Matthew 5:18)

"But the very hairs of your head are all numbered." (Matthew 10:30)

k. God is just (innocent; blameless and without guilt; orderly; righteous; in a moral sense, upright; honest; having principles of rectitude; conforming to the laws) and requires us to keep accurate records and measurements.

"The Rock! His work is perfect, For all His ways are just; A God of faithfulness and

Notes

without injustice, Righteous and upright is He." (Deuteronomy 32:4, NASB)

"You shall have just balances, just weights, a just ephah, and a just hin: I am the LORD your God, who brought you out from the land of Egypt." (Leviticus 19:36, NASB)

Mathematics enables mankind to demonstrate His justice when dealing with one another.

7. God gave man the gift of mathematical language and blessed him with the ability to describe His ways (operations), His measurement (magnitude), and quantity using symbols (numbers).

   "Out of the ground the LORD God formed every beast of the field and every bird of the sky, and brought them to the man to see what he would call them; and whatever the man called a living creature, that was its name." (Genesis 2:19, NASB)

8. The laws of mathematics are completely pure (unmixed, free from defilement, true) and incorruptible (inflexibly just and upright).

   "Great are the works of the LORD; They are studied by all who delight in them. Splendid and majestic is His work; And His righteousness endures forever. He has made His wonders to be remembered." (Psalm 111:2–4, NASB)

   "[T]o obtain an inheritance which is imperishable and undefiled and will not fade away, reserved in heaven for you." (1 Peter 1:4, NASB)

   "[F]or you have been born again not of seed which is perishable but imperishable, that is, through the living and abiding word of God." (1 Peter 1:23, NASB)

9. God commanded us to use numbers to identify quantity (that property of anything which may be increased or diminished). God blessed man with the ability to express quantity using numbers.

   "As the LORD commanded Moses, so he numbered them in the wilderness of Sinai." (Numbers 1:19)

10. God requires man to keep accurate records and measurements. Mathematics enables man to maintain justice, especially in standard weights and measures, thereby supporting and maintaining peace based upon Christian character.

    "Justice, and only justice, you shall pursue, that you may live and possess the land which the LORD your God is giving you." (Deuteronomy 16:20, NASB)

    "A just balance or scales are the Lord's; all the weights of the bag are His work (established on His eternal principles)." (Proverbs 16:11, Amplified)

11. Mathematics is a God-given tool (instrument or that which is subservient to the execution of a plan or purpose) and, when applied to the sciences, technology, economics, music, fine art, architecture, business and industry, helps man fulfill the dominion mandate.

    "God created man in His own image, in the image of God He created him; male and female He created them. God blessed them; and God said to them, 'Be fruitful and multiply, and fill the earth, and subdue it; and rule over the fish of the sea and over the birds of the sky, and over every living thing that moves on the earth.'" (Genesis 1:27–28, NASB)

    Applications of the Tool of Mathematics:

    - Science: researching and studying the systems and processes of the universe
    - Technology: applying science for human benefit and God's glory
    - Economics: working, saving, inventing, investing, launching, and managing enterprises
    - Business and industry: applying these principles in the marketplace for optimum use
    - Education: teaching these principles to the next generation
    - Fine arts: glorifying God's handiwork and cultivating man's aesthetic tastes

12. God's purpose in mathematics is to bring us to total maturity and completeness, "unto a perfect man, unto the measure of the stature of the fulness of Christ" in agreement with Ephesians 4:13.

Notes

"[F]or the equipping of the saints for the work of service, to the building up of the body of Christ; until we all attain to the unity of the faith, and of the knowledge of the Son of God, to a mature man, to the measure of the stature which belongs to the fullness of Christ."
(Ephesians 4:12–13, NASB)

13. Mathematics serves man in achieving "unity with diversity." Individuals and nations are in constant tension as they struggle in dealing with physical and scientific problems. God desires us to work together with others to govern His creation for His glory.

"I . . . implore you to walk in a manner worthy of the calling with which you have been called, with all humility and gentleness, with patience, showing tolerance for one another in love, being diligent to preserve the unity of the Spirit in the bond of peace." (Ephesians 4:1–3, NASB)

Mathematics Describes the Excellence of God's Character

"If our hearts are right, we love God above all things, as the sum of excellence and all the attributes which can communicate happiness to intelligent beings. The Christian loves God with the love of complacency in his attributes, the love of benevolence towards the interests of his kingdom, and the love of gratitude for favors received." (Noah Webster, 1828)

"Mathematics proclaims that:

1. God is unchangeable
2. That God is a God of order
3. That God is a God of system
4. That God is a God of precision
5. That dependability is one of God's attributes
6. That God's infinitude is perhaps more clearly revealed in Mathematics than in any other school subject."[1]

Therefore, the relation of mathematics to God is that it is a reflection of His very essence, His nature, and His character. It is not a created thing, but is of God. God is immutable; hence, truth is not altered by the next human discovery.[2]

Because man is made in God's image (Genesis 1:26–30; Genesis 2:7; 1 Corinthians 11:7), his language imitates the works (naming, Genesis 2:19; 1:4; governing, Genesis 1:28; Psalms 22:28; improving, Genesis 2:15; 1:31), and rest of God (Genesis 2:2; Exodus 20:11)."[3] Man is created with the ability to understand some aspects of God and this creation. His reasoning is not always right because he is not able to comprehend God entirely. Man's knowledge is limited. (Psalm 94:10b–12; Job 32:8–9; Isaiah 40:26; 51:6; Proverbs 30:24–28)

The existence of the gift of language enables man to communicate with one another. Men have one racial origin (Acts 17:26), they share one common nature, the image of God (Genesis 1:26–27; 5:1–3), and they have been given the gift of language as part of their equipment to fulfill the cultural mandate (Genesis 2:19–23). Non-Christians can and do make significant contributions to mathematics and science. Because they know mathematical truth, they know something about God and it is beneficial to them. Therefore, Christians and non-Christians share mathematical truths because Christianity is true, because God is who He is and man is created in the image of God. Work in mathematics can have relevance to the Christian when it is motivated by the love of God, in keeping with God's ways and Word, and directed to the glory of God.

Man learns first by imitation. We learn mathematics first, from those who demonstrate it to us followed by formal instruction in its principles at a stage in life where it is possible to form understanding. This instruction sequence teaches one to depend upon principles (absolutes, internals) and to see facts as things that confirm principles but do not create them. It teaches one to see numbers as unique and distinct governed by ways (operations) of combining or separating them (Christian self-government with union, rather than socialism). Faith first, followed by understanding, produces a secure, interdependent, worshiper of God and His

1 Excerpted from Dr. Mark Fakkema's *Christian Philosophy and Its Educational Implications,* Book 3. Chicago, IL: National Association of Christian Schools, ca. 1946.

2 Gary North, ed. "Essays in the Van Til Perspective," *Foundations of Scholarship*. Vallecito, CA: Ross House Books, 1976, 186.

3 Ibid.

Notes

ways. The result in the student is that he uses his knowledge and understanding to solve problems to the benefit of mankind to God's glory!

Man, created by God in His image, has the ability and need to:

Walk with God (Genesis 3:8): Man, made in the image of God, can reason and understand mathematics based upon the revelation of God's Word, the Bible.

Work (Genesis 2:15): Man can apply what he's learned to solve practical mathematical problems that glorify God and benefit mankind.

Worship God (Genesis 4:1–5): As man learns and understands more about mathematics as God's expressed nature and character, his love for God, the Great Mathematician, the Sovereign God of creation, culminates in worship! "The *love* of God is the first duty of man, and this springs from just views of his attributes or excellencies of character, which afford the highest delight to the sanctified heart. Esteem and reverence constitute ingredients in their affection, and a fear of offending him is its inseparable effect." (*love*, Webster's 1828 *Dictionary*)

When the study of mathematics is separated from God and His Word, it lacks the inspiration of the Holy Spirit and renders the subject meaningless to the student, who loses sight of what symbol manipulations imply about real quantities. Traditional math courses are an endless series of memorizing and forgetting facts and procedures that make little sense to students. This method of teaching mathematics is not only ineffective, but seriously stunts mathematical reasoning and skillful problem solving. This method shows students how to solve a certain type of problem, and then has them practice it in class and homework. The method does not teach why the operations work or reveal the greatness of God and His excellent character.

Christian methods enable students to spend time understanding mathematics, thinking mathematically, and solving practical problems. Students do not waste time learning computational procedures that can be done by a calculator without understanding why the computations work or when they should be applied. These Christian methods provide students with numerous opportunities to solve complex and interesting problems as well as to read, write, and discuss mathematics. The Christian methods described in this guide will actively direct students to the principles that govern the subject and produce valid solutions to meaningful problems. The teacher will enjoy using many appealing strategies to problem solving.

Notes

Vocabulary of America's Christian History and Government

Chain of Christianity®

God's use of individual men and nations to move the Gospel and liberty for the individual westward and the effecting of Christianity into the civil sphere. See the Christian History Timeline for clarity on the major links in history.

Character

"The peculiar qualities, impressed by nature, a habit or God which distinguish him from others"; the perfect standard and principle of Christian character is Jesus Christ, the "express image" of God, the Father. (Hebrews 1:3); Therefore, Christian character is the expressly peculiar stamp, mark, or character of Christ engraved upon an individual; character is causative and its effect is the history and heritage of the individual.

"History requires a just knowledge of character, to investigate the sources of action."

(Mercy Otis Warren in Hall's *The Christian History of the American Revolution: Consider and Ponder*, 158c)

America's heritage of Christian character is exemplified by the Pilgrim dynamic through these character qualities:

Faith and Steadfastness
Brotherly Love and Christian Care
Diligence and Industry
Liberty of Conscience

Christian Self-Government

Christ governing through the power of the Holy Spirit in the heart and mind of an individual by consent. Self-control is man's response to the knowledge of God's will. Christian self-government makes God's Law the requirement of the heart and is the basis of our American Christian constitution. Civil government flows from the hearts of individuals.

"Let divines and philosophers, statesmen and patriots, unite their endeavors to renovate the age, by impressing the minds of men with the importance of educating their little boys and girls, of inculcating in the minds of youth the fear and love of the Deity and universal philanthropy, and, in subordination to these great principles, the love of their country; of instructing them in the art of self-government, without which they never can act a wise part in the government of societies, great or small; in short, of leading them in the study and practice of the exalted virtues of the Christian system."

(Samuel Adams, "Rights of the Colonists," 1772, in Hall's *The Christian History of the Constitution of the United States*, Vol. I, xiv.)

Conscience

"Internal or self-knowledge, or judgment of right and wrong; the faculty, power or principle within us, which decides on the lawfulness or unlawfulness of our own actions and affections, and instantly approves or condemns them."

(Webster's 1828 *Dictionary*)

"That little spark of celestial fire that tells us right from wrong." (George Washington from *The Rules of Civility*.) Right and wrong must be learned from the Scriptures.

"Conscience is the most sacred of all property." (James Madison, *Essay on Property*, March 29, 1792.) Therefore, conscience must be exercised by consent requiring careful stewardship.

Dominion

Sovereign or supreme authority, the power of governing and controlling; man created in God's image is given the responsibility of subduing and having dominion over all creation.

(Genesis 1:26–28)

Notes

Government

The flow of power or the exercise of authority that regulates, directs, controls, or restrains; the source of all authority, law, and government is found in God and defined in His Word.

God-ordained spheres of government:

Family—Genesis 2:24
Church—Matthew 16:18
Civil—Romans 13:1–7

Individuality

The state of being distinct and separate as created and maintained by God; God's Principle of Individuality is the primary principle of American Christian history, government, and education.

"[A]ll things were created through him, and for him: And he is before all things, and in him all things consist." (Colossians 1:16b–17, NKJV)

"For who maketh thee to differ from another? and what hast thou that thou didst not receive?"
(1 Corinthians 4:7)

Law

A rule prescribed for regulating the social actions of people; in the Old Covenant, God framed a fundamental Law, the Ten Commandments, for the government of men and the protection of their lives and property. In the New Covenant, Christ fulfilled the Law.

"This is the covenant that I will make with them after those days, saith the Lord, I will put my laws into their hearts, and in their minds will I write them." (Hebrews 10:16)

"Think not that I am come to destroy the law, or the prophets: I am not come to destroy, but to fulfil. For verily I say unto you, Till heaven and earth pass, one jot or one tittle shall in no wise pass from the law, till all be fulfilled." (Matthew 5:17–18)

Liberty

Freedom from restraint; consists in the power of acting as one thinks.

"For as [a man] thinketh in his heart, so is he."
(Proverbs 23:7)

"[W]here the Spirit of the Lord is, there is liberty."
(2 Corinthians 3:17)

Principle

The cause, source or origin, that from which a thing proceeds; seeds; foundation, that which supports a series of actions or of reasoning.

Providence

The act of providing for the future; the continual care and superintendence that God exercises over His creatures and whose final aim is the fulfillment of His purpose in creation; "by Divine Providence is then understood God Himself." (Webster's 1828 *Dictionary*) Providence is the key to understanding history.

"But as it is written, Eye hath not seen, nor ear heard, neither have entered into the heart of man, the things which God hath prepared for them that love him." (1 Corinthians 2:9)

Most historians who wrote before 1900 viewed history from the providential approach.

"Nothing gives history a greater superiority to many branches of literature, than to see in a manner imprinted, in almost every page of it, the precious footsteps and shining proofs of this great truth, viz. that God disposes all events as supreme Lord and Sovereign; that he alone determines the fate of kings and the duration of empires; and that he transfers the government of kingdoms from one nation to another because of the unrighteous dealings and wickedness committed therein."
(Historian Charles Rollin in Hall's *The Christian History of the American Revolution: Consider and Ponder*, 605)

Notes

Thinking Governmentally

Thinking governmentally is a powerful tool of reasoning that teaches the student to identify the flow of force or power in any given situation—internally and externally. It inculcates the habit of beginning the process of reasoning or problem solving by seeking the source or cause of what is known or seen. It also aids the student in dealing with his own character. It teaches the student to search the Scriptures first and to reason with the revelation of truth. "And that from a child thou hast known the holy scriptures, which are able to make thee wise unto salvation through faith which is in Christ Jesus. All scripture is given by inspiration of God, and is profitable for doctrine, for reproof, for correction, for instruction in righteousness: That the man of God may be perfect, throughly furnished unto all good works." (2 Timothy 3:15–17)

Noah Webster, father of American education and scholarship, wrote in his *Letters to a Young Gentleman Commencing His Education (Rudiments 9–10)*:

> As men are furnished with powers of reason, it is obviously the design of the creator, that reason should be employed as their guide, in every stage of life. But reason, without cultivation, without experience and without the aids of revelation, is a miserable guide; it often errs from ignorance, and more often from the impulse of passion. . . . Let it then be the first study that occupies your mind, to learn from the scriptures the character and will of your maker; the end or purpose for which he gave being and intellectual powers, and the duties he requires you to perform, and all that regards faith and practice, the scriptures furnish the principles, precepts and rules, by which you are to be guided. Your reputation among men; your own tranquillity of mind in this life; and all rational hope of future happiness, depend on an exact conformity of conduct to the commands of God revealed in the sacred oracles.

American Christian education, the Principle Approach®, emphasizes thinking governmentally in reasoning, particularly in the subject of history. Government by God, or Christian self-government, occurs through the individual's *voluntary consent*. The goals of Christian education are to fit the child with the character of Christian self-government and to reclaim the character of Christian self-government—the character of the constitutional Christian republic.

A philosophy of education is based upon a philosophy of government. Abraham Lincoln stated that "the philosophy of education in the classroom is the philosophy of government in the next generation." Your view of the principles of teaching and learning is determined by your idea of "who or what is exercising control" and ultimately becomes the authority, source, or presuppositions of your worldview. Every form of government is the result of a philosophy of education. God ordained three governmental institutions: home, church, and civil government.

The Christian idea of man and government is that God ordained civil government for man's good to protect man's God-given life, liberty, and his property (both material and internal—conscience, ideas, etc.) The Christian view of government is first internal or causative and then external, with civil government the effect, as each individual acknowledges the sovereignty of God in his life.

Thinking governmentally applies the definition of *government* to reasoning and asks, "who or what controls, directs, regulates, or restrains in this situation?" and then reasons as shown below:

THE PRINCIPLE APPROACH SHOWS HOW THE INTERNAL GIVES RISE TO THE EXTERNAL*	
INTERNAL ⟶	EXTERNAL
Causative Primary Invisible Unseen	Effect Secondary Visible Seen

*James B. Rose, *A Guide to American Christian Education for the Home and School: The Principle Approach.* Palo Cedro, CA: American Christian History Institute, 1987, 29.

Pagan versus Christian Views

Pagan	Christian
Views of History	
1. All things came into being through chance happenings. 2. Man's environment is the cause of his actions. 3. The goal is to change society economically, politically, etc. 4. Success is in the ability to adapt and to adjust to society. 5. Purpose of history: Man's story and man's glory.	1. All things were created by God. (John 1:3) 2. Man's heart is the cause of his actions. (Mark 7:20–23) 3. The goal is to become a new creation. (2 Corinthians 5:17) 4. Success is in overcoming through Christ. (Joshua 1:8; 1 John 4:4) 5. Purpose of history: God's story and His glory.
Views of Man	
1. Man is simple and primitive, but becoming better. 2. Human progress is in altering the external environment to produce better internal character. 3. The effect: Man is in bondage to his environment.	1. Man is fallen and needs a Savior. 2. Human progress is in altering the internal nature/character to produce a better environment. 3. The effect: Free, independent, self-governing individual.
Views of Education	
1. Evolutionary 2. Pragmatic necessity of technology drives the wheels of education. 3. Exerts external influences by— • stimulating (subject) • motivating (consume) • enculturating (conform) • indoctrinating (confuse) —*Making environment the cause* 4. The effect: Control the individual by changing behavior and hold in bondage for a lifetime of dependency on others' thinking and solutions.	1. Wholistic (John 1:3) 2. Appeals to the internal by: • inspiring the heart with the Word of God • consecrating the mind to Christ • cultivating the new man • instructing in the knowledge of salvation and fear of the Lord —*Making conscience the cause* 3. The effect: Freedom through Christian character growth and a renewed mind for a lifetime of Biblical reasoning and problem solving.
Views of Mathematics	
1. Man's reason is autonomous in mathematics. 2. Mathematics is a tool that enables man to create order out of a universe of chaos. 3. Mathematics is a neutral, secular discipline; a mental construct; an intellectual game. 4. The pragmatic necessity of technology and the needs of the state drive the wheels of mathematics. 5. Mathematics has little application to the sciences or the "real" world.	1. Creator God is the Author of mathematics, the Great Mathematician. 2. Mathematics is the language God used to create the structure of the universe, the patterns of which describe the laws of His handiwork and verify His Word. 3. Mathematics is a disciplined thought structure that describes the numerical and spatial aspects of God's creational structure. 4. Mathematics plays an important role in Christ, His Story on the Chain of Christianity®. 5. The principles of mathematics contribute to unify the whole body of knowledge and must be studied in the context of creation as the foundation for all technical and scientific logic.

Gaining a Christian Worldview in Mathematics

An individual's worldview determines his view of mathematics. If you view the triune God as the source of creation then: 1) man is dependent on this all-knowing and all-loving God, who reveals Himself and His ways so man can know Him and govern himself accordingly; and 2) mathematics is an expression of the very character and nature of God, who has revealed Himself through His Word (written), His creation (general), and His Son (personal).

God has given mankind alone the gift of reason, in order that he might arrange and systematize the revelation of God (the laws of nature) for himself. Man needs reason to discover what the law of nature directs. However, the system man develops does not legislate what is possible or what is actual. The system is subject to reasoning with the revelation of Scripture, not independent of it. For the Christian, God legislates what is possible or impossible for man; however, for the unbeliever or pagan, man determines this for himself.

> Law signifies a rule of action and is applied indiscriminately to all kinds of action, whether animate or inanimate, rational or irrational. Thus we say, the laws of motion, of gravitation, of optics, or mechanics, as well as the laws of nature and of nations.
> (Blackstone)

The Christian and pagan worldviews differ on the foundational points of mathematics and science because one's worldview is influenced by his religious belief system. What an individual believes concerning the origin, purpose, and destiny of the cosmos affects the way he perceives mathematics and science. Mathematics is not a neutral discipline. In his book, *Mathematics: Is God Silent?*, James Nickel writes "In its presuppositional base, mathematics either thrives or dies. In the civilizations of antiquity, we have seen that mathematics progressed for a few centuries, then stagnated due to a false worldview. We have also noted the great creative mathematical stirrings that took place in a culture steeped in the Biblical worldview. Today, many mathematicians and scientists philosophically deny the worldview that birthed modern science. . . . Francis Schaeffer observes that 'the worldview determines the direction such creative stirrings will take, and how—and whether the stirrings will continue or dry up.' It is a fact that, in the twentieth century, more work has been done in mathematics than all other centuries combined. If mathematics should die in a culture steeped in humanism, the belief in the autonomy of man's mind, why all this activity? Schaeffer continues, 'Later, when the Christian base was lost, a tradition and momentum had been set in motion, and the pragmatic necessity of technology, and even control by the state, drives science on, but . . . with a subtle yet important change in emphasis.'"[1]

For the Christian committed to Scripture, the most important fact about mathematics must be its relation to the Lord (Acts 17:28; 1 Chronicles 29:11). The most basic question to ask about mathematical structures and laws is this: Are they aspects of creation or of God? What is the relation between mathematics and the living God?

[1] James Nickel, *Mathematics: Is God Silent?* Vallecito, CA: Ross House Books, 1990, 64.

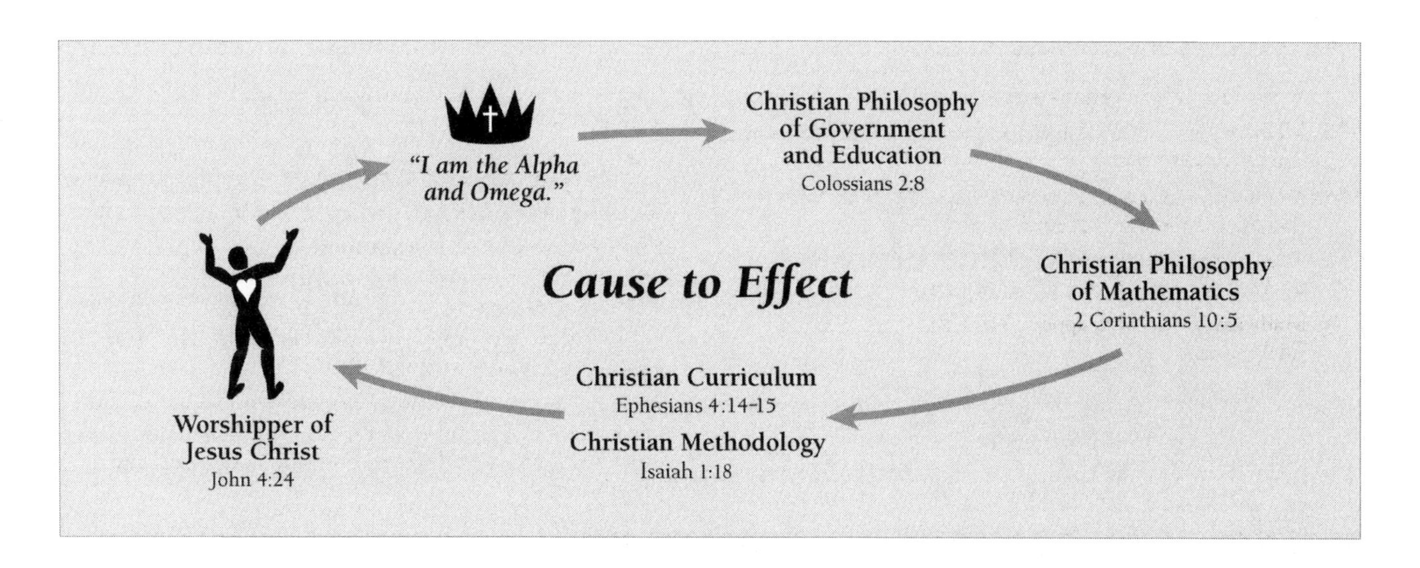

Notes

Guiding Principles for Teaching and Learning Mathematics

Principle One: Mathematics Is Unchangeable and Universal

Mathematics is an expression of the attributes of God's divine nature and character. These attributes are immutable. (Malachi 3:6) "Jesus Christ the same yesterday, to day, and for ever." (Hebrews 13:8) Mathematics describes God's eternal and infinite nature, and is reliably the same on every continent of the earth and throughout the universe. The principles governing mathematics for Adam, Noah, Abraham, Moses, Paul, Columbus, Wycliffe, and America's Pilgrims, patriots, and pioneers are the same principles that govern mathematics today. Mathematics runs true throughout all generations, a very dependable connection with our past, and its history a powerful testimony for Christ and liberty. Mathematics is a discipline that has the potential to lead the skeptic to the eternal Mathematician.

Principle Two: The Principles of Mathematics Are Demonstrable

"It is the peculiar excellence of mathematics, that its principles are demonstrable." (Webster's 1828 *Dictionary*) The principles of mathematics are easily demonstrated. The youngest learner can actually "see the unseen" when the principles of mathematics are shown to him and this facilitates learning. Discerning truth develops faith and confidence rather than skepticism in the learner. The demonstrated truth of the principles of mathematics causes the learner to trust in God and His ways and draws the learner to Him.

Principle Three: Mathematics Is a Language

As a language, mathematics specifically communicates ideas about quantities as well as relationships between quantities. Because God created man to be a reasoning, speaking creature, he is able to process and express his thoughts orally or in written form. When man thinks and communicates mathematical ideas, quantities, or relationships, it is often referred to as mathematical poetry—the equation. Man uses this tool to prove thoughts true or absurd when properly applied. Man's linguistic abilities to encode (notation, express) or decode (numeration, impress) mathematical thoughts and to store information in the brain are the functions of language.

Principle Four: Mathematics Is an Art and a Science

The primary sense of the word *art* is strength and power, hence skill. The art of anything answers the purpose for which it is intended. In mathematics, this is the system of rules governing the discipline and serving to facilitate the performance of certain actions. The science of mathematics is its principles. When teaching mathematics, emphasize the "art" before the "science." Both are necessary to achieve mastery.

Principle Five: Mathematics Is Best Learned by First Visualizing Quantity

One of the results of mastering mathematics is the attainment of the knowledge of quantity and the facilitation of working with quantities. Biblical principles of economics encourage the use of machinery to facilitate labor and increase productivity. Counting may be made less difficult by using an instrument to facilitate calculating quantities, and develops the art of computation in the learner through visualization of quantities. Counting is laborious, tedious, slow, prone to errors, ignores place value, and hinders developing the art of computation because it keeps numbers unitized rather than visualized as quantities.

The art of computing is well developed when individual units (individuality) become quantity (unity). It is the American Christian governmental principle of unity with union. The art of computation unites two or more unique entities into one quantity with ease. This is achieved by using

Notes

consistent language to speak numerically without ignoring place value. The art of computation rightly discourages unitized counting and encourages visualizing (recognizing) quantity, which facilitates computation. When one visualizes or recognizes bananas, one sees them as one bunch, or a quantity of bananas. Similarly, the abacus, with its color-coded base-ten, subbase-five beads, develops the ability to recognize quantities that don't have to be counted every time they are used to facilitate mental computation. Having a mental image of a quantity based on fives and tens aids the development of the art of computation. Having a unitary image (counting) hinders the rapid computing of quantities.

Principle Six: Mathematics Is Best Understood by Analysis and Reason

The science of numbers is best learned by analysis and reason (see Five-Step Method to Problem Solving, *NPMG*, pages 110–111). *Analysis* is the separating of a compound body into its constituent parts and *reason* refers to thought that is alleged in words, as the cause of opinion, conclusion, or determination. The Christian view of the learner upholds teaching and learning by analysis and reason.

Breaking a compound problem into its constituent parts aids the problem-solving process. The thought process of the learner works from cause to effect (absolutes to rules). This confirms God's principles and rules as reliable and builds faith in the heart of the individual. This analysis and reason technique is more time consuming and more difficult than traditional approaches; however, it restores the learning model to one of effort and mastery and away from gifted and talented. When applying effort, learners have ample room to make errors while learning without hampering their development. Effort applied enables each student to learn from his own errors and the errors made by others when openly discussed in love. Effort is causal to learning! This enables the development of American Christian character—the overcoming character of Christ.

Not everyone has the same mathematical ability, although everyone has the potential to become mathematically literate! Each individual is responsible to God to develop fully his God-given potential. The qualities of Christian character should be exercised in fulfilling this responsibility to God. Scripture instructs us to be diligent and to apply effort in a steady and constant manner. (Proverbs 10:4; 12:24, 27; 21:5; 22:29; Joshua 22:5) Orderly, regular, and methodical (Psalm 37:23) effort causes learning. Determination and attentiveness (Hebrews 2:1; Psalm 119:9–11; 1 Corinthians 3:10) encourage the student to take heed of God and His ways. Man obtained the ability to understand mathematical concepts when God made him in His image with great intelligence. Adam was given the faculty of speech—an ability to use the knowledge of words. All of Adam's faculties were bestowed on him by God's supernatural power. This ability to communicate was given to Adam and his offspring before the creation of Eve. Scripture reveals that God possessed speech before creation. He spoke the world into existence. Man is created in God's image, his mind has all the mental faculties of God's mind. Man was created for God's purpose. The mathematical faculty is in the mind of man because it was first in the mind of God. Adam's intelligence is just one expression of what it means to be made in the image of God's intelligence.

Principle Seven: A Teacher Teaches Mathematics Best

"I would advise you to make the Mathematics your principal and almost sole object. Consider Natural philosophy as quite secondary, because the books will teach you that as well as any master can. Whereas Mathematics require absolutely the assistance of a teacher." (Thomas Jefferson)

Children learn by imitating what is modeled for them. Communicating the principles of mathematics requires the effort of a mathematics teacher who clearly demonstrates the principles to the learner. The teacher needs a thorough knowledge of the subject, a love for the subject, and an aptitude to teach the subject.

Christian History of Mathematics Timeline

Eternity Past

The uncreated and immortal triune God in Eternity. The Eternal I AM!

"'I am the Alpha and the Omega,' says the Lord God, 'who is and who was and who is to come, the Almighty.'" (Revelation 1:8, NASB)

"Now to the King eternal, immortal, invisible, the only God, be honor and glory forever and ever. Amen." (1 Timothy 1:17, NASB)

"Father, . . . thou lovedst me before the foundation of the world." (John 17:24)

"[J]ust as He chose us in Him before the foundation of the world, that we would be holy and blameless before Him." (Ephesians 1:4, NASB)

Creation

B.C.

God spoke creation into existence—*ex nihilo.*

Michelangelo Buonarroti, *Creation of Adam*, 1512, Sistine Chapel, Vatican City

In the beginning, God spoke, and by the power of His word, the heavens and the earth came into existence.

"In the beginning God created the heaven and the earth. And the earth was without form, and void; . . . And God said, Let there be light: and there was light." (Genesis 1:1–3)

God created mathematics to establish and uphold order in the physical universe.

"In the beginning was the Word, and the Word was with God, and the Word was God. He was in the beginning with God. All things came into being by Him, and apart from Him nothing came into being that has come into being. In Him was life; and the life was the Light of men. The Light shines in the darkness, and the darkness did not comprehend it." (John 1:1–5, NASB)

"For since the creation of the world His invisible attributes, His eternal power and divine nature, have been clearly seen, being understood through what has been made." (Romans 1:20, NASB)

Reasoning with the revelation of God's Word

God created man in His image to have fellowship with Him and to worship Him. He endowed him with the gifts of language and reasoning and placed him in the Garden of Eden. (Genesis 1:26; 2:8, 19–20)

Man was fashioned to take dominion and rule over creation through an intimate, worshipful relationship with the infinite, personal God. He observed God's orderly creation and its governing principles. Coupled with revelation from God, he used his gift of reason to classify creation for man's use and to glorify God.

The fall of man's nature through sin.
(Genesis 3)
Revelation rejected! Reasoning corrupted!
Mathematics fragmented.
(Romans 1)

Noah and the Flood
(Genesis 6:14–22; 7:1–16; 8:1–22)

"The created world, as a result of God's speech, bears within it from top to bottom a kind of quasilinguistic character . . . [T]hrough God's act of creation, things in the world themselves become wordless voices to the praise of God." (Vern Polythress)

"All things that came into being by Him" were spoken into existence through the language of mathematics and reveal the attributes of the nature and character of the Creator. This cause-to-effect reasoning, in conjunction with his relationship to God, resulted in Adam worshiping the Creator, not the creation. God's creation is replete with both numerical and spatial relationships.

"It is the duty of man, as a dominion bearer, to observe this reality and classify it for use. Man, made in the image of God, is able to observe the physical creation and formulate relationships and consequences that both and explain and predict. Throughout the history of mathematics, we find man doing just that."
(James Nickel, *Mathematics: Is God Silent?*, 2001, 6)

Man is deceived and his nature and ability to reason are corrupted. Faith in human reason alone supplants divine revelation.

Reason alone is a miserable guide when separated from divine revelation and always results in death, decay, and disunity. It produces fragmentation of life, including mathematics. Autonomous man begins to worship the creature rather than the Creator.

"For even though they knew God, they did not honor Him as God or give thanks, but they became futile in their speculations, and their foolish heart was darkened. Professing to be wise, they became fools, and exchanged the glory of the incorruptible God for an image in the form of corruptible man and of birds and four-footed animals and crawling creatures. Therefore God gave them over in the lusts of their hearts to impurity, so that their bodies might be dishonored among them. For they exchanged the truth of God for a lie, and worshiped and served the creature rather than the Creator, who is blessed forever. Amen."
(Romans 1:21–25, NASB)

The descendants of Adam and Eve were fruitful and highly skilled in various crafts such as metal works and carpentry. However, they became more and more wicked. God was sorry that He had made man on earth and prepared to destroy mankind in a great flood. But Noah found grace in the sight of God and received from God directions for building an ark, 450 feet long, 75 feet wide, and 45 feet high. (Genesis 6:8–15)

Biblical evidence of applied mathematics is seen in the construction of the ark: architecture (designing), construction (building), numbering animals (tallying), and food storage (measuring, distributing).

In the ancient, postdiluvian civilizations, mathematics played a prominent role such as: "tables of squares and square roots, tables of cubes and cube roots, solutions to cubic equations, the theory of compound interest (exponential functions), and even the solution of quadratic equations." (Nickel 2001, 6)

Sumerian/Babylonian Civilization

3000

The **Babylonians** invented the abacus. They had an advanced number system, the most amazing aspect of which was the construction and use of tables to aid calculation. They divided the day into 24 hours, each hour into 60 minutes, and each minute into 60 seconds.

Numeral Hieroglyphs

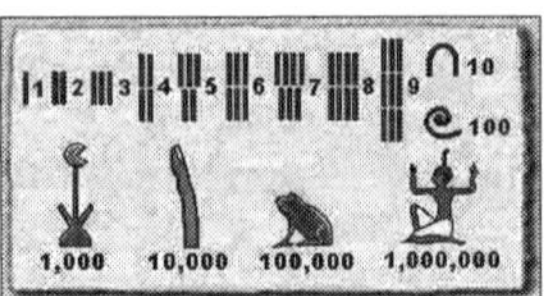

Egyptian Civilization

Egyptian mathematics was elementary. Pyramids, granaries, and business transactions reveal the rudiments of algebra, geometry, and trigonometry.

Moses and the Moral Law

1450

The Ten Commandments
(Exodus 20:1–17)

Weights and measures were a part of the moral law. (Proverbs 20:23) God instructed Moses to conduct a *census*, to *partition*, *sort*, or *arrange* the Israelites by tribes in *strategic* locations. (Numbers 1:1–4)

Mathematics was required for solving problems and useful purposes such as census-taking, partitioning, sorting, arranging, and strategizing. Joseph measured and stored grain.

Greek Civilization

800

The development of the structure and theory of mathematics as we know it today began in the classical age of Greece and extended to 600 A.D. **The Greeks** systematized mathematics from prior civilizations. Almost all the famous Greek philosophers were mathematicians who sought answers to the basic questions of life based upon human reason alone. (Nickel 2001, 6–7)

Heroic Age of Mathematics

600

Thales of Miletus (ca. 624) one of the Seven Sages of ancient Greece and the father of ancient Greek philosophy. He founded the Ionian School and is credited with identifying the nature of numbers.

500

Pythagoras (582?–500?) one of the most famous mathematicians; believed "the number ruled the universe." Founded a school for scientific research in number theory, geometry, music, and astronomy. Coined the word *mathematics*, and developed the proof by deductive reasoning and the Pythagorean Theorem: $a^2 + b^2 = c^2$.

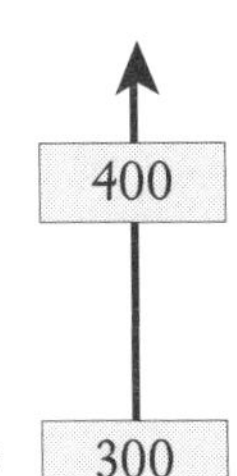

400

Zeno of Elea (495–435) whose baffling pagan paradoxes introduced a schism into mathematical thought regarding time, space, and infinity that is discussed even today.

Golden Age of Greek Mathematics

300

The mathematics of classical Greece tended toward the absolutization of abstract thought, which produced useful and practical results. Mathematicians applied irrational numbers to their calculations, which resulted in the development of trigonometry. The Greeks correlated the study of mathematics to the book of nature, laying the foundation for modern science. Their language became the universal language of commerce and trade.

Euclid

Euclid (330–275) father of geometry and deductive reasoning and the most prominent mathematician of antiquity. He wrote *Elements*, a compilation of three centuries of Greek mathematical achievements. No work, except the Bible, has been more widely used, edited, or studied or has exercised a greater influence on scientific thinking. Euclid applied deductive reasoning to the mathematical method.

200

Archimedes

Archimedes of Syracuse (287–212) discovered hydrostatic pressure.

The Greek and Roman civilizations introduced geographical measurement and nautical navigation.

Eratosthenes (ca. 230) accurately measured the circumference of the earth using basic propositions derived by Euclid.

100

Hipparchus

Hipparchus (ca. 140) father of trigonometry, which he developed to help solve astronomical problems.

The Greek culture produced significant developments in both mathematics and science by establishing the correlation between mathematics and the study of the design of nature—the very basis of modern scientific work.

In preparation for the coming of the Messiah and the spread of His Gospel, God inspired Greek mathematical thought for practical use by men and nations.

Great Roman Empire

Although the **Romans** contributed little to mathematics, they applied Greek mathematical thought to impressive engineering projects, architectural monuments, medicine, and agriculture. Their contributions in the realm of civil engineering enabled the Gospel to go westward over land and sea.

Bernhard Plockhurst
Jesus Blesses the Children
Windows of McKendree, 1910

Jesus Christ
Focal Point of History

A.D.

Jesus Christ, the first and living Principle of representation and substitution—the Incarnate One.

"In the beginning was the Word, and the Word was with God, and the Word was God. . . . And the Word was made flesh, and dwelt among us, (and we beheld His glory, the glory as of the only begotten of the Father,) full of grace and truth."
(John 1:1, 14)

Biblical reasoning, coupled with revelation, is restored!

Man now has the potential through salvation in Christ and the indwelling of the Holy Spirit to be transformed by the renewing of his mind. (Romans 12:2)

"For WHO HAS KNOWN THE MIND OF THE LORD, THAT HE WILL INSTRUCT HIM? But we have the mind of Christ."
(1 Corinthians 2:16, NASB)

Mathematics was limited to the trades, accounting, and timekeeping.

Apostle Paul
The Gospel Travels Westward
(Acts 16:9–12)

60

Christianity moves westward across the Roman roads during the missionary journeys of Paul. As a tentmaker, Paul utilized the art of computation and applied the principles of geometry to his craft.

Byzantine and Saracen Civilizations

600

Islamic armies pushed Greek scholars into Constantinople (A.D. 640), where their mathematical thought was absorbed. The **Arabs** introduced several important mathematical concepts to Europe that were borrowed from the Hindus: the base ten (decimal) system, positional notation, the number zero, and negative numbers.

al-Khowarizmi

800

Mohammed al-Khowarizmi (780–850) Arabic father of algebra, who developed algorithms and the rudiments of the science of equations. He wrote a book on algebra (A.D. 830), which was translated into Latin, the language of medieval scholarship.

1000

Translations of Arabic mathematics into Latin (1000–1250) enabled arithmetic and geometry to support each other. They created a new interest in mathematics and science. The revival of learning in Latin Europe took place during the Crusades. No one "could boast of being a mathematician who was not a Moor, a Jew, or a Greek."
(Carl B. Boyer, *A History of Mathematics*, 1991, 25)

Fibonacci

1100

Leonardo of Pisa (Fibonacci) (1180–1250) Italian who introduced Arabic numerals to Europe. His book, *Liber Abaci*, combined Islamic and Christian medieval thought—that arithmetic and geometry are connected and support each other. He discovered and named the golden ratio, or the "Divine Proportion." Kepler noted that by the end of the twelfth century, the leading and most original mathematician in the world, Fibonacci, came from Christian Italy.

The period was one of transition from an older to a newer point of mathematical view.

Roger Bacon

1200

Roger Bacon (1214–94?) English Franciscan monk renowned for his mathematical discoveries. "God has not created the world for the sake of the universal man, but for the sake of individual persons." (Roger Bacon, *Communia Naturalium*, 1264)

The Bible in English

Translation of the Bible into the languages of the commoner gave rise to the Protestant Reformation.

1300

John Wycliffe (1320?–84) "morning star of the Reformation," translated the Vulgate Bible into Middle English.

Scripture in the hands of the individual renewed thinking and reasoning as well as mathematical thought.

Nicole Oresme (1333?–82) Frenchman who introduced notation for fractional exponents and pioneered early methods of calculus.

1400

Johannes Gutenberg (1480–68) invented the printing press in Germany (1455), which eventually fulfilled the dream of William Tyndale, placing "the Bible in the hands of the plow boy."

Mathematical writings were printed as well. This dispersed new and productive mathematical ideas, causing an explosion of invention and enterprise.

Michael Stifel (1487–1567) German mathematician who applied positive and negative symbols (+ and -) in mathematical notation. His *Arithmetica Integra* became the most important of all sixteenth century algebras.

da Vinci

Leonardo da Vinci (1452–1519) Italian artist and inventor who designed the first mechanical calculator (1500).

Copernicus

Nicolaus Copernicus (1473–1543) Polish trigonometer and astronomer who recognized the correlation between mathematical thought and nature. He praised God, saying, "So great is this divine work of the Great and Noble Creator!" He rejected geocentrism for heliocentrism. (Nicolaus Copernicus, *On the Revolution of the Heavenly Spheres*, 1543)

Columbus

The pathway of the seas was opened for the westward move of the Gospel.

1492 The application of mathematics to cartography and navigation ushered in the **Era of Exploration.**

1500 **The Protestant Reformation** birthed the scientific revolution (1500–1700), which was based upon the Biblical belief that the God of the Bible created the universe and designed it in a rational and orderly way.

François Viète (1540–1603) Frenchman who contributed to the advancement of arithmetic, algebra, trigonometry, and geometry. He is credited with decimals, roots, and coefficients.

Napier

John Napier (1550–1617) Scotsman who developed logarithms.

Galileo

Galileo Galilei (1564–1642) This Italian professor of mathematics (Pisa and Padua) and scientist invented the geometric and military compasses. He was known as a "mathematical practioner." Galilei believed that the laws of nature brought clear testimony of a Lawgiver.

Kepler

Johannes Kepler (1571–1630), a German Lutheran who developed the principle of continuity and the laws of planetary motion. He glorified God in his discoveries and praised Him in all his writings.

Descartes

René Descartes (1596–1650) French philosopher and mathematician who developed analytic geometry and the Cartesian coordinate system.

Bonaventura Cavalieri (1598–1647) Italian mathematician and professor who was the first to appreciate the value of logarithms.

Cavalieri

1600 **Pierre de Fermat** (1601?–65) Frenchman who is considered one of the great mathematicians of the seventeenth century and shared with Pascal the formulation of the Theory of Probability.

Evangelista Torricelli (1608–47) Italian mathematician who worked with the area and tangent of cycloids.

Fermat

Christian Founding

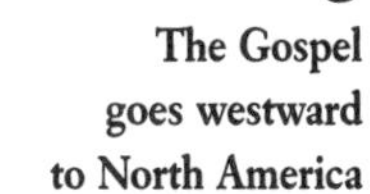

The Gospel goes westward to North America

George Boughton, *Pilgrims Going to Church,* 1867, 29″ x 52″, Henry Luce III Center, New York Historical Society.

1620

The seed of the first Christian constitutional republic is planted by the Pilgrims and Puritans. Harvard College is founded in 1636.

Pascal

Blaise Pascal (1623–62) French philosopher and mathematician whose Christian thought developed conics, the arithmetic machine, and the Pascal Triangle.

Huygens

Christiaan Huygens (1629–95) Dutch mathematician and physicist who invented the pendulum clock.

Newton

Sir Isaac Newton (1642–1727) Englishman widely regarded as the greatest mathematician of all time. "His insight into physical problems and his ability to treat them mathematically has probably never been excelled." (Howard Eves 1976, in Nickel, 122) He developed differential calculus and gave expression to the Binomial Theorem and the Universal Law of Gravitation. Authored *Principia,* which explained the true source of the beautiful system of the universe —the Sovereign Lord over all.

Gottfried Liebnitz (1646–1716) German mathematician who furthered the development of integral calculus.

1700

Bernoulli

Daniel Bernoulli (1700–82) Belgian-born Swiss Christian mathematician who perfected calculus and developed the Theory of Hydrodynamics, which led to the Flight Principle. Three generations of Bernoullis produced eight mathematicians.

Leonhard Euler (1707–83) Swiss Christian mathematician who developed pure analytical mathematics and is considered the premier notation builder of all time. His Biblical faith invited sharp criticism from atheists such as Voltaire and Diderot.

American Christian Republic

The first Christian constitutional republic is founded based upon Biblically-derived governmental principles.

Arnold Friberg, *The Prayer at Valley Forge,* 1975, 45″ x 72″, personal collection.

1776

Nathaniel Bowditch (1773–1838) Father of American mathematics and author of "the seaman's bible," *The New American Practical Navigator.*

Bowditch

Karl Gauss (1777–1855) German mathematical genius, called the "prince of mathematicians," who aided in the development of systematic arithmetic (number theory). His *Disquisitiones Arithmeticae* is one of the great classics of mathematical literature. He enjoyed the art of mental computation as a child.

Jean Poncelet (1788–1867) developed the pole and polar lines associated with conics, which led to the Principle of Duality.

Expansion and Erosion

Michael Faraday (1791–1867) English physicist, chemist, and mathematician who identified the Law of Electromagnetic Induction (one of the five mathematical equations that changed the world).

Charles Babbage (1791?–1871) English mathematician who invented the difference and the analytical "calculating engines."

1800

George Boole (1815–64) English mathematician who wrote the *Mathematical Analysis of Logic*, emphasizing that logic should be associated with mathematics rather than metaphysics.

Clausius

Rudolf Clausius (1822–88) Prussian mathematician and physicist who gave expression to the Second Law of Thermodynamics.

Leopold Kronecker (1823–91) Prussian mathematician who solved systems of polynomial equations.

Maxwell

James C. Maxwell (1831–1879) English mathematician best known for his very successful derivation of the electromagnetic wave equations and who was influential in urging mathematicians and physicists to use vectors.

George William Hill (1838–1914) Most notable American mathematician and analyst responsible for the Theory of Linear Differential Equations with Periodic Coefficients.

Georg Cantor (1845–1918) Russian-born German mathematician who is best known as the formulator of the Set Theory and for his discovery of transfinite numbers.

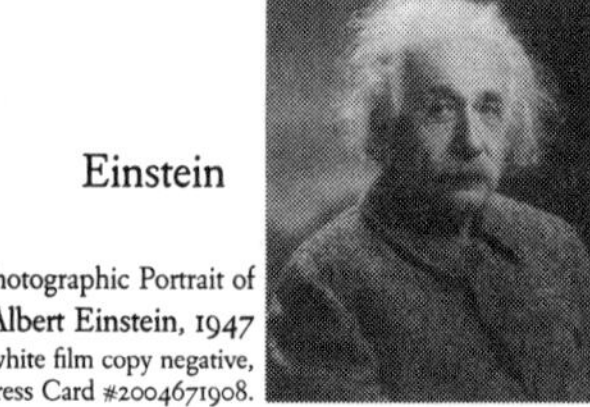

Einstein

Oren Jack Turner, Photographic Portrait of Albert Einstein, 1947 black and white film copy negative, Library of Congress Card #2004671908.

Albert Einstein (1879–1955) German-born American physicist and mathematician who identified the relationship between mass and energy in his *Special* (1905) and *General* (1915) *Theories of Relativity*. He determined that the most fundamental form of energy is light as expressed in the equation, $E=mc^2$.

1900

The twentieth century contributed more advancements in mathematics than all other centuries combined, particularly in the development of intellectual theories.

Neumann

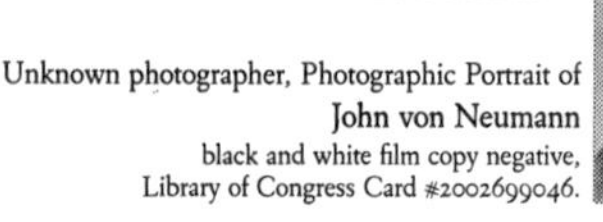

Unknown photographer, Photographic Portrait of John von Neumann black and white film copy negative, Library of Congress Card #2002699046.

John von Neumann (1903–57) Hungarian-born American mathematician who published a definition of ordinal numbers when he was twenty that is still used today. A Princeton math professor who pioneered computer science and significantly contributed to the development of logical design, he advocated the adoption of the bit as a measurement of computer memory and solved problems in obtaining reliable answers from unreliable computer components.

Mandelbrot

Benoit Mandelbrot (1924–) Hungarian-born mathematician largely responsible for the present interest in fractal geometry. He showed how fractals can occur in many different places in both mathematics and elsewhere in nature using computer graphics.

21st Century

Restoration

Your Picture

Your place in His Story!

(Write your name)

Restoring Christ, His Story to mathematics through renewed thinking: reasoning with the revelation of God's Word in mathematical thought, problem solving, and applications to science.

"If mathematics is the basis of creation, its nature revelatory of God, and its purpose is to glorify God, the Christian teacher must de-secularize mathematics for his students. That is, he must polish away the patina of secularization with which mathematics has become encrusted so its true, God-reflecting nature shines through." (Larry Zimmerman 1980)

"The chief end of man is to glorify God and to enjoy Him forever." (*Westminster Catechism*)

O Worship the King

by Robert Grant

O worship the King all glorious above,
And gratefully sing His wonderful love;
Our Shield and Defender, the Ancient of Days,
Pavilioned in splendor and girded with praise.

O tell of His might and sing of His grace,
Whose robe is the light, whose canopy space;
His chariots of wrath the deep thunderclouds form,
And dark is His path on the wings of the storm.

Thy bountiful care what tongue can recite?
It breathes in the air, it shines in the light,
It streams from the hills, it descends to the plain,
And sweetly distills in the dew and the rain.

Frail children of dust, and feeble as frail,
In Thee do we trust, nor find Thee to fail;
Thy mercies how tender, how firm to the end,
Our Maker, Defender, Redeemer and Friend!

Eternity Future

Chapter Three
An American Christian Methodology for Teaching and Learning Mathematics

But there is a spirit in man,
And the breath of the Almighty
gives him understanding.
(Job 32:8, NKJV)

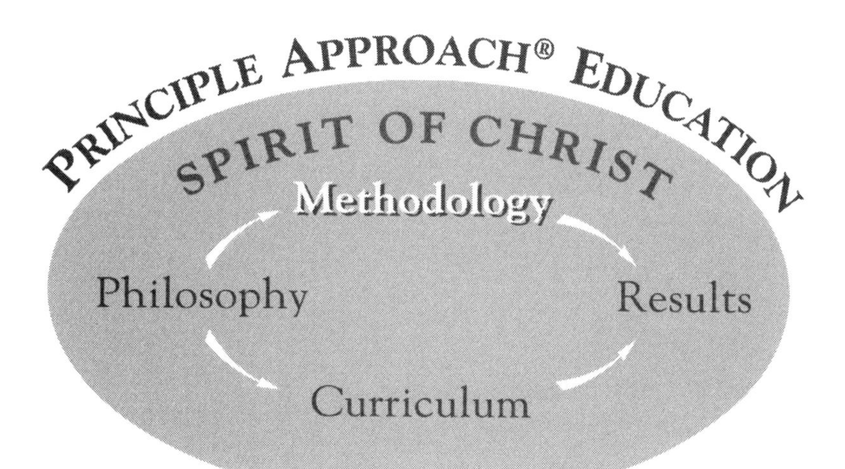

Notes

Introducing an American Christian Methodology

The Principle Approach® restores the Biblical inspiration to the study of any subject in the curriculum including mathematics. This is the one and only solution to the widespread sense of boredom that prevails among students concerning the very idea of learning. All students enjoy learning when there is meaning and purpose to what is being taught. Without Biblical inspiration, all subjects are rendered "boring." Teachers must accept the challenge to inspire their students by using real problems chosen from the world that surrounds the learners and in which they are interested. Children use their senses to learn, so let us make use of the physical world to solve physical and practical problems while making the subject appealing to the learner. Show the learner the glory of God reflected through mathematics. That is inspirational!

"And one cried to another and said: 'Holy, holy, holy is the LORD of hosts; The whole earth is full of His glory!'" (Isaiah 6:3, NKJV) All creation declares the glory of God. Let us reveal the glory of God to our students by studying the physical creation and describing it in the language of mathematics. This grants internal meaning and purpose to mathematics. The true purpose of mathematics is to make God known. Mathematics affirms the Creator and makes us accountable to Him. A deep study of mathematics and science leads to Christ—the Creator God. The Principle Approach to mathematics education teaches mathematics from the foundation or the source of mathematics—God. It is the only way to teach mathematics and restore it to its Gospel purpose!

According to Webster's 1828 *Dictionary*, *method* is defined as "(1) [a] suitable and convenient arrangement of things, proceedings or ideas; . . . convenient order for . . . comprehending any complicated subject. . . . Without method, business of any kind will fall into confusion. (2) Way; manner." To teach effectively, let us imitate Jesus' methods. Jesus used parables as concrete illustrations taken from daily life or nature familiar to the learner in order to explain an abstract truth. The abstract is contained in the concrete. Let us apply this approach to the teaching and learning of mathematics. Seek to present the concrete as a foundation for the abstract, the known as a foundation for the unknown.

When subjects lead nowhere they lose their life and lose inspired students also. Nothing quenches the spirit or love of learning faster than teaching that has no internal, external, and eternal meaning or purpose that can be understood and appreciated by the learner. As teachers using the Principle Approach, we must reconnect subject matter to Life Himself. We must reconnect mathematics to the power source from which it flows. The best way to do this is to teach the subject in its historical context—His Story of the subject and how it has advanced the spread of the Gospel, and, thus, liberty. When the subject is severed from His Story, it cuts off the flow of life to the subject. Hence, the secularization of mathematics has severed math from its life, so our students and nation suffer. If a limb were cut from a robust tree, the limb would contain residual life for a short period of time. Yet the limb's future is determined because it is no longer connected to its source of life, the robust tree. Ultimately, it is doomed to die after exhausting its residual life and merely reflects a decaying and lifeless shell of a structure. This lifeless structure is what mathematics has become in the minds and hearts of our youth, especially because it has been severed from its Christian Biblical roots. History teaches us that the first principles to be learned are the ones that are useful to solve practical problems in the physical realm and improve man's ability to take dominion over God's creation.

Teachers must accept the challenge to inspire their students by using real problems chosen from the world that surrounds the learners and in which they are interested.

God created the human mind with the capacity to observe, explore, formulate, explain, predict through the gift of reason, and express the results mathematically. Let us teach mathematical principles (abstractions) by using concrete pictures, analogies, and parables first, as means to the end of laying a foundation and building "line upon line" from the known to the unknown.

Notes

Let deductive reasoning serve as the means to verify results. Thoughtless computation does not produce mature growth. Knowledge for its own sake is worthless and puffs up. It is worthless unless it is connected to understanding and properly and wisely applied. The teacher must enable the student to know how to do mathematics (art), to know why the methods of mathematics work (science, understanding), and to know how to apply these methods to new and unfamiliar applications (wisdom).

How Learning and Understanding Mathematics Happen
(The relationship of the whole to its parts)
Understanding = Truth (mathematical) + Instruction + Reflection
Understanding = T + I + R
Wisdom = Understanding + Experience (application)
or
Wisdom = T + I + R + E

Working Definitions from Webster's 1828 *Dictionary*

abstract, *v.t.* To separate ideas by the operation of the mind; to consider one part of a complex object, or to have a partial idea of it in the mind.

instruction, *n.* (1) The act of teaching or informing the understanding in that of which it was before ignorant; (2) Precepts conveying knowledge.

learning, *n.* (1) The knowledge of principles or facts received by instruction or study; . . . (2) Knowledge acquired by experience, experiment, or observation.

reflection, *n.* The operation of the mind by which it turns its views back upon itself and its operations; the review or reconsideration of past thoughts, opinion or decisions of the mind, or of past events.

understanding, *n.* The faculty of the human mind by which it apprehends the real state of things presented to it, or by which it receives or comprehends the ideas which others express and intend to communicate. The understanding is called also the *intellectual faculty*. It is the faculty by means of which we obtain a great part of our knowledge. (Luke 24:27–32; Eph. 1:8)

As *Rabboni*, or Master Teacher, Jesus modeled for us the best method of teaching by taking an abstraction and linking it through good instruction to the learner's personal experience and observation. In imitation of Jesus, we must realize that taking an abstraction (mathematical truth) and linking it through good instruction, study and observation to the experience of the learner best achieves understanding. In imitation of Jesus, our methods must include these ingredients for our students to be as successful as they can be in learning mathematics. To develop powerful mathematical thinking in students, one must emphasize understanding; they must understand why things are the way they are by reasoning upon observable quantities using mathematical principles and deriving rules that support the facts. Guiding the student's reflections pertaining to his work with quantities encourages understanding. This enables students to develop personally meaningful mathematical relationships. Mathematics, as the expression of the nature and character of a living God, imparts joy and enlightenment to the successful learner of mathematics. It is no longer merely the correct arrangement of meaningless symbols according to established usage. It produces more powerful thinkers who think mathematically in the fullest sense of the phrase.

Biblical Methodology Objectives

1. Methods must reconnect mathematics to its source of life—God through His Story (Job 32:8).
2. Methods must be Biblical.
3. Methods must include:

   Truth (mathematical)
   + Inspired instruction
   + Reflection
   ———————
   Understanding

4. Methods must link understanding to experience resulting in wisdom.

A Teaching Plan for Mathematics in the Principle Approach®

1

THE NOAH PLAN

Fifth Grade

MATHEMATICS OVERVIEW

"For since the creation of the world His invisible attributes, His eternal power and divine nature, have been clearly seen, being understood through what has been made, . . ." (Romans 1:20, NASB)

"Where were you when I laid the foundation of the earth? Tell Me, if you have understanding, Who set its measurements, since you know? Or who stretched the line on it? On what were its bases sunk? Or who laid its cornerstone, . . . ?" (Job 38:4-6, NASB)

Mathematics is the science of quantity; of whatever can be measured or numbered. —Webster's 1828 *Dictionary*

Mathematics is the language of God expressed at creation, the patterns of which laid the structure of the universe and describe the laws of His handiwork. —*Noah Plan Mathematics Curriculum Guide*

Arithmetic is the science of numbers or the art of computation. The various operations of arithmetic are performed by addition, subtraction, multiplication, and division. —Webster's 1828 *Dictionary*

Principles Demonstrated and Taught:

- God's Principle of Individuality
- Principle of Representation
- Commutative Principle of Addition
- Associative Principle of Addition
- Principle of Symmetry
- Principle of Place Value

Purposes:

- Reveal God and His divine nature and character through mathematics.
- Identify and demonstrate the principles governing mathematics.
- Reason from the principles of mathematics and apply them to problem solving.
- Teach the place of mathematics on the Chain of Christianity moving westward.
- Form the character of American Christian mathematics.

Skill Objectives:
(Build on previous grade-level achievements.)

- Introduce the science of numbers.
- Attain proficiency in associative, commutative, and distributive principles of mathematics.
- Develop and use algebraic thinking.
- Apply percentage with and without the element of time.
- Attain competence in measuring with the metric system.
- Increase the vocabulary of mathematics.
- Enrich and/or integrate with other subjects in the curriculum: mathematical games; poems, crafts, and music; engineering tools and projects; local businesses; local newspapers—bank ads, sale ads, and finance section.
- Develop a character that is self-governed, self-educating, productive, and able to reason based on Biblical understanding from a mathematical perspective.

Apply percentage with and without the element of time.

Preserving the American Christian Spirit

THE NOAH PLAN ©1997 THE FOUNDATION FOR AMERICAN CHRISTIAN EDUCATION 251

Review the Fifth Grade Mathematics Overview. Select the unit to be developed.

2

Fifth Grade Mathematics Curriculum
The Science of Numbers

Purposes | Principles | Definitions | Foundations | Methods | Resources | Performance Accomplishments

Examine the Fifth Grade Mathematics Curriculum chart, *NPMG*, pages 28–29.

Highlight details to be taught in this unit.

3

Quarterly Plan Sheet for Teaching Mathematics

Quarter ______ Week ______ Teacher ______ Grade ______

Week	Foundations	Numbers	Numeration/Notation	Measurement	Operations	Problem Solving
1						
2						
3						
4						
5						
6						
7						
8						
9						

May be duplicated

Using the Quartely Plan Sheet for Teaching Mathematics, *NPMG*, page 84, identify the math component to be taught on the weekly schedule.

4

Refer to sample lesson plans for inspiration and guidance.

5

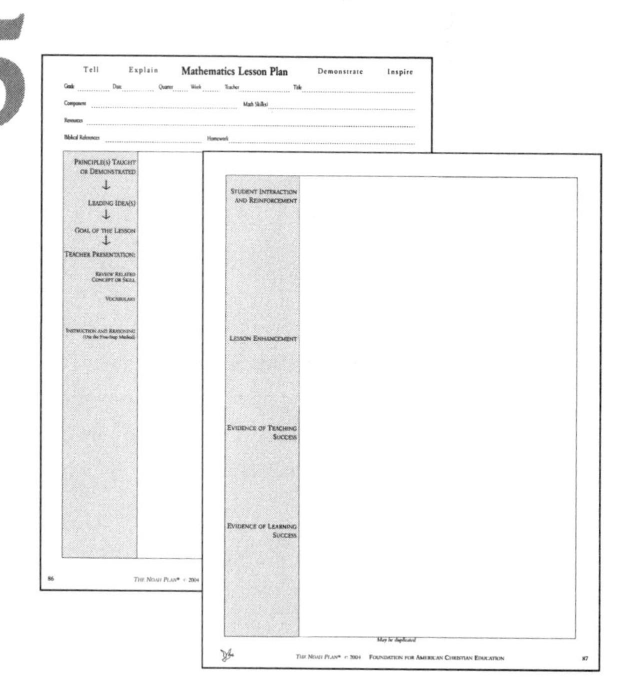

Write the lesson plan using the format, *NPMG*, pages 86–87.

Developing Subject Curriculum

Research

verb: To search or examine with continued care; To seek diligently for the truth

noun: Diligent inquiry or examination in seeking facts or principles; continued search after truth

Principle Approach Application
To search the vocabulary of the subject being studied for its Biblical source and purpose.

Identify the following as you research:

1. Biblical foundation
2. Vocabulary (define from Webster's 1828 *Dictionary*)
3. Christian history of the subject
4. Key individuals
5. Key events
6. Key documents
7. Contributions that advanced the Gospel and liberty for the individual
8. Literature of the subject
9. Geographical settings/maps
10. Art, music, drama
11. Leading ideas
12. Bibliography/citations
13. Inspiration for use with students
14. Student activities to enrich

Reason

verb: To deduce inferences justly from premises

noun: A faculty of the mind by which it distinguishes truth from falsehood and good from evil, and which enables the possessor to deduce inferences from facts or from proposition

Principle Approach Application
To reason from Biblical truths and apply them to the subject being studied. Reasoning builds upon truth already researched.

Ask and answer these leading questions:

1. What are the Biblical principles of this subject?
2. What are the other principles of this subject?
3. Has God been glorified and His character and nature been identified?
4. What are God's purposes for the subject? (These should be deduced from God's Word using definitions from Webster's 1828 *Dictionary* written out in your own words.)
5. How has this subject contributed to the spread of the Gospel and individual liberty?
6. What have we learned in the study of this subject about the formation of character?
7. What have we learned in the study of this subject about stewarding our consciences?
8. What have we learned in the study of this subject about the art of Christian self- and civil government?
9. What additional principles have we learned from the study of this subject?

in the Principle Approach®

Relate

verb: To tell; to recite;
To restore;
To ally by connection

Principle Approach Application
To expound or explain thoroughly the meaning and application of Biblical truth.

Relate the subject to your students by:

1. Selecting textbook(s) and/or identified readings from the literature available on the subject, particularly primary sources
2. Applying leading ideas and questions to guide classroom discussions and assigned reason questions
3. Creating written assignments
4. Identifying drill and practice work
5. Designing projects or crafts with grade-appropriate instructions and helps
6. Locating maps for use
7. Developing demonstrations, experiments, and/or participatory activities
8. Creating a timeline
9. Designing a chart to summarize information
10. Writing a simple dramatic presentation
11. Creating a classroom display
12. Designing field studies or tours
13. Locating and filing poetry, literature, art masterpieces, and songs to enrich lessons
14. Planning a special day celebration
15. Creating a bulletin board that highlights a principle or leading idea being taught
15. Developing the ability to tell stories in an animated way

Record

verb: To write or enter in a book; for the purpose of preserving authentic or correct evidence;
To imprint deeply on the mind or memory;
To cause to be remembered

Principle Approach Application
To write, organize, and file in a binder the complete study of the subject in a way that causes it to be remembered and serve as a permanent record for future use.

Make a permanent teacher record by:

1. Maintaining a thorough notebook study
2. Making copies of outstanding student work and filing for future reference
3. Videotaping performances and special events
4. Photographing projects, bulletin boards, costumed students, and events
5. Video or audio taping special guests

Make a permanent student record by:

1. Encouraging thorough student notebooks, into which is filed all written work, maps, quizzes, tests, memory work, research reports, field study records, and the Notebook Grade Sheet
2. Taping student presentations or performances in speech, oration, drama, and music
3. Duplicating photographs for each child's notebook

Teaching the Art of Learning
by Leading Ideas and Principles

Is not the great defect in our education today, that although we succeed in teaching our students "subjects," we fail lamentably on the whole in teaching them how to think? They learn everything, except the art of learning!
(Dorothy Sayers, "The Lost Tools of Learning" [a paper read at Oxford University], 1947)

Leading Idea:

A tool of reasoning that guides the student's thinking along a pathway or a basic concept that helps organize the student's thinking. It bridges the concrete (the known, the facts, the story, the passage of text, etc.) to the abstract (the unknown, the principle), and vice versa, so that the student can formulate ideas and solve problems for himself.

Leading,

1. *ppr.* Guiding; conducting; preceding; drawing; alluring;
2. *a.* Chief; principal; capital; most influential; as a leading motive;
3. Showing the way by going first.

Idea, *n.* [L. *idea*; . . . Gr. . . . to see, . . .]

1. Literally, that which is seen; hence, form, image, model of any thing in the mind; that which is held or comprehended by the understanding or intellectual faculties. . . . The attention of the understanding to the objects acting on it, by which it becomes sensible of the impressions they make, is called by logicians, perception; and the notices themselves as they exist in the mind, as the materials of thinking and knowledge, are distinguished by the name of ideas.
2. Image in the mind.

(Webster's 1828 *Dictionary*)

The teacher must think beyond isolated subject matter (information) and teach principles and objectives that transcend the facts. Rather than spoon-feeding predigested answers, he guides and directs the student's thinking along a pathway with leading ideas and questions, so that the student can figure out answers for himself.

Leading Idea

The Pathway of Reflective Thinking

?

Concrete	**Reasoning**	**Abstract**
Subject Matter Information, Facts	With the Revelation of God's Word —Truth	Principles "Real State of Things"
What Is Known		The Unknown
External — Effect	*Muse Consider Ponder*	**Internal — Cause**

But there is a spirit in man: and the inspiration of the Almighty giveth them understanding.
(Job 32:8)

Teaching the Art of Learning
by Masterful Teaching

A pupil is not above his teacher; but everyone, after he has been fully trained, will be like his teacher.
(Luke 6:40, NASB)

Christian teachers should be more than preachers and dispensers of information. Masterful teaching teaches the student how to learn and inspires Biblical reasoning!

Goal of artful learning: consecrated mind

1. Primary level of learning:

   Build skills of literacy:
   reading, writing, composition.

   Memorization

2. Elementary level of learning:

   Build skills of thinking and reasoning: language.

3. High School level of learning:

   Build the skills of articulate expression:
   logic, rhetoric.

4. Higher level of learning:

   Mastery of subjects (information)

   Incorporate thinking and reasoning, language mastery, and articulate expression.

   Lifetime love of learning!

Role of the teacher in teaching the art of learning

1. Inculcate the habit of reasoning with the revelation of God's Word (truth).
2. Teach how to "rightly divide the word of truth." (2 Timothy 2:15)
3. Break big questions into smaller, more manageable parts.
4. Help students clarify their thoughts by rephrasing or asking questions.
5. Pose thought-provoking questions.
6. Help keep discussions focused.
7. Encourage students to explain things to each other.
8. Help students find what they need to know by showing them how to use available resources and tools of learning.
9. Ensure that students value each others' views.

Teaching the art of learning by asking questions

1. Probe meanings.
2. Request reasons and evidence.
3. Facilitate elaboration.
4. Keep discussions from becoming confusing.
5. Provide incentive for listening to what others have to say.
6. Lead to fruitful comparisons and contrasts.
7. Highlight contradictions and contrasts.
8. Elicit implications and consequences.

Quarterly Plan Sheet for Teaching Mathematics

Quarter ______________ Week ________ Teacher ________________ Grade ______

Week	Foundations	Numbers	Numeration/Notation	Measurement	Operations	Problem Solving
1						
2						
3						
4						
5						
6						
7						
8						
9						

Distinctives of the Principle Approach® Lesson

The Principle Approach lesson creates a specific effect in the student.

1. **The lesson appears in a subject taught in the context of America's Christian history and government.**

   Result: Students

   a) Learn the chronology of God's Story and can identify every subject by it
   b) Understand God's purpose for each subject as it is used to further the Gospel and liberty for the individual

2. **The philosophy affirms the full value of each student.**

   Result: Affirmation

   a) Satisfies students' intellectual needs
   b) Appeals to their hearts and consciences for a self-government-under-God response
   c) Presents appropriate challenges to build character

3. **The lesson is governed by a Christian teacher who has himself mastered the subject and the Biblical philosophy of education.**

   Result: Students are engaged in producing a product—their own education. Therefore, they are able to

   a) Research Biblically
   b) Think reflectively
   c) Develop and write curriculum, leaving a record of scholarship
   d) Use the tools and practice the habits of Christian scholarship
   e) Develop a love of lifetime learning

4. **Each lesson is guided by Biblical principles.**

   Result: Biblical Principles

   a) Maintain the integrity of the subject, consecrating it
   b) Provide truths in the lesson, which fit into the whole revelation of God's purposes in history
   c) Enliven the subject and inspire students

5. **The teacher guides the students' thinking with leading questions, calling upon reflective learning.**

   Result: Students

   a) Observe
   b) Identify
   c) Discover
   d) Articulate for themselves

6. **The vocabulary of the subject is defined and taught.**

   Result: Students

   a) Master preciseness of language
   b) Masterfully articulate ideas and thoughts and inculcate perspicuity
   c) Study logic and rhetoric

7. **Notes are recorded in an organized way in the students' notebooks**

   Result: Notebooks

   a) Make the lesson productive and reflective rather than just another reading or writing assignment
   b) Provide students with permanent records of their learning

8. **The the teacher is a living textbook.**

   Result:

   Every classroom is a reflection of a unique individual responding to the high calling of American Christian education.

9. **Principle Approach education produces a gentle, inquiring, dignified spirit within the school.**

   Result: This spirit in turn produces

   a) A readiness for learning
   b) An honoring, Godly, wholesome character
   c) A dynamic that envelops and warms the student, cultivating, inspiring, and consecrating them for God's call and purposes for their lives

10. **The end product of the American Christian Principle Approach is self-governing, Christ-reflecting character, which is enterprising and productive. It produces the kind of future leader we as parents and educators pray for daily—the kind that will change the world for the glory of God.**

11. **What is the fruit?** Students who

    a) Are independent Christian scholars
    b) Have a lifelong love for learning and reflection
    c) Have Biblical worldviews
    d) Have Christian characters
    e) Have hearts to serve Christ and community

Tell • Explain **Mathematics Lesson Plan** Demonstrate • Inspire

Grade ________ Date ________ Quarter ____ Week ____ Teacher ____________ Title ______________________

Component ______________________________ Math Skill(s) ______________________________

Resources ____

Biblical References ____________________ Homework ______________________________

PRINCIPLE(S) TAUGHT OR DEMONSTRATED ↓ LEADING IDEA(S) ↓ GOAL OF THE LESSON ↓ TEACHER PRESENTATION: REVIEW RELATED CONCEPT OR SKILL VOCABULARY INSTRUCTION AND REASONING (Use the Five-Step Method)	

May be duplicated

STUDENT INTERACTION AND REINFORCEMENT	
LESSON ENHANCEMENT	
EVIDENCE OF TEACHING SUCCESS	
EVIDENCE OF LEARNING SUCCESS	

May be duplicated

Tell • Explain **Mathematics Lesson Plan** Demonstrate • Inspire

Grade *3* Date *9/23/00* Quarter *1* Week *2* Teacher *Mrs. Ricciardi* Title *Numbers Reveal God's Nature & Character*

Component *Foundations* Math Skill(s) *Reasoning with the Word of God*

Resources *Bible, Webster's 1828 Dictionary*

Biblical References *Gen 1:31; Ps 147:5; Heb 13:8* Homework *Paraphrase from class notes, "How numbers reveal God's character."*

PRINCIPLE(S) TAUGHT OR DEMONSTRATED ↓	*1. God is a God of order. (Genesis 1:31)* *2. God is infinite. (Psalm 147:5)* *3. God does not change. He is the same yesterday, today, and forever. (Hebrews 13:8)*
LEADING IDEA(S) ↓	*Numbers demonstrate (reveal) God's character.*
GOAL OF THE LESSON ↓	*Guide students in their understanding of God's character through the study of arithmetic.*
TEACHER PRESENTATION:	
REVIEW RELATED CONCEPT OR SKILL	*Biblical foundation of arithmetic: definitions, origin, purpose* *Question students about the previously taught Biblical foundations.*
VOCABULARY	• *reveal—to disclose; to make known from heaven; to show; to make known something before unknown (Eph. 3:3)* • *infinite—without limits; that which will have no end* • *order—series; a manner or way of arranging*
INSTRUCTION AND REASONING (Use the Five-Step Method)	*1. Write title on board and discuss its meaning.* *2. Look up new vocabulary using Webster's 1828 Dictionary.* *3. Look up Scriptures that support definitions.* *4. Reason with and guide the children to the Biblical principle from the leading idea.* *5. Record these research notes on the board.* *6. Request that students describe the largest number they know and then add one (1) to it.* *7. Repeat process until students grasp the idea of God's infinite (never-ending) nature.*

STUDENT INTERACTION AND REINFORCEMENT	1. *Look up new vocabulary with the teacher.* 2. *Look up Bible verses with the teacher to support definitions.* 3. *Students research, reason, and relate how God's character is never-ending (infinite) as demonstrated by numbers and addition.* 4. *Students record findings (Biblical documentation and arithmetic examples) in their Math Notebooks.*
LESSON ENHANCEMENT	*Have students look up other Scriptures to support the goal of the lesson:* *Malachi 3:6* *James 1:17*
EVIDENCE OF TEACHING SUCCESS	*Every student actively engaged in lesson.* *Lesson satisfied each learning style.*
EVIDENCE OF LEARNING SUCCESS:	*Each student can articulate today's lesson in his own words the next school day.* *Each student can answer reason questions successfully, such as:* • *What do Hebrews 13:8, Psalm 147:5, and Luke 1:28 teach us about God?* • *How do these Scriptures relate to numbers?*

Tell • Explain **Mathematics Lesson Plan** Demonstrate • Inspire

Grade *3* Date *11/00* Quarter *2* Week *4* Teacher *Mrs. Ricciardi* Title *Multi-digit Subtraction*

Component *Operations (Subtraction)* Math Skill(s) *Simplified Subtraction Algorithm*

Resources *Bible, Webster's 1828 Dictionary; student slates; board*

Biblical References *John 3:30; Prov. 13:11* Homework *RightStart Worksheet of problems to answer*

PRINCIPLE(S) TAUGHT OR DEMONSTRATED

The minuend and subtrahend must be of the same kind.
- The difference is the same in kind as the minuend and subtrahend.
- The difference equals the minuend minus the subtrahend.
- The minuend equals the difference plus the subtrahend.
- The subtrahend equals the minuend minus the difference.

LEADING IDEA(S)

Only by obedience to the law and love of God can man ever find the happiness for which God made him. Therefore, man must **decrease** so that He might **increase.**

↓

GOAL OF THE LESSON

The purpose of this lesson is to have the students learn one of five ways to subtract. This lesson teaches the simplified subtraction algorithm with trading taken from Numbers 1:21 and Numbers 26:7—the census of Israel's fighting men.

↓

TEACHER PRESENTATION:

REVIEW RELATED CONCEPT OR SKILL

VOCABULARY

INSTRUCTION AND REASONING (Use the Five-Step Method)

Vocabulary of subtraction: taking a lesser number from a greater number; greater; lesser
multi-digit: multi=many; digit=number under 10, so called from counting on the fingers 1, 2, 3, 4, 5, 6, 7, 8, 9

Use Webster's 1828 Dictionary to define: **decrease, diminish, subtract, remainder, minuend.**
"He must increase, but I must **decrease.**" (John 3:30)
"Wealth gotten by vanity shall be **diminished:** but he that gathereth by labor shall increase." (Proverbs 13:11)

Numbers chapter 25 describes a plague that greatly reduced some of the tribes.
1) Read Numbers 1:21 and record the number of Reubenites before the plague (46,500—minuend).
2) Read Numbers 26:7 and record the number of Reubenites after the plague (43,730—remainder).
3) Calculate the number of Reubenites killed by the plague.
4) Compare the second census with the first, and see how the populations changed.

46,500 men during first census (before the plague)
\- 43,730 men during second census (after the plague)

Beginning on the left:
1) Point to the 4. Ask, "Are there enough ten thousands to subtract four ten thousands?" [Yes]
2) Then point to the 6. Ask, "Are there enough thousands to subtract three thousands?" [Yes]
3) Point to the 5. Ask, "Are there enough hundreds to subtract seven hundreds?" [No]
4) Ask, "How can we get more hundreds?" [From the thousands]
5) Underline the 6 and explain that the underline reminds us we need to trade.
6) Ask, "How many thousands will we have after the trade?" [5]
7) Write the 5 above the 6. See below.

```
   5
 46,500
-43,730
```

8) Ask, "How many hundreds do we have?" [15]
Write the 15 above the 5. See below.

```
   5 15
 46,500
-43,730
```

9) Ask, "Are there enough tens to subtract three tens?" [No]
10) Ask, "How can we get more tens?" [From the hundreds]
11) Underline the 5, explaining it reminds us we need to trade.
12) Ask, "How many tens will we have after the trade?" [10]
Write 10 above the 0 as shown.
13) Ask, "How many hundreds will we have after the trade?" [14]
14) Write the 14 above the 15 to indicate the number of hundreds remaining after the trade. Then cross out the 15.
15) Now the actual subtraction can begin. Proceed from **Left to Right**.

```
     14
  5 15 10
 46,5 0 0
-43,7 3 0

     14
  5 15 10
 46,5 0 0
-43,7 3 0
  2,7 7 0
```

STUDENT INTERACTION AND REINFORCEMENT

- Practice and participation: Multi-digit subtraction without trading on slates (teacher-assisted).
- Practice and participation: Multi-digit subtraction with trading on slates (teacher-assisted).
- Practice and participation: Multi-digit subtraction with and without trading on slates (unassisted).
- Presentation: Every student solves a subtraction problem on a slate without teacher assistance. Upon completion, a student is selected to present to the entire class his reasoning which brought him to his solution.

LESSON ENHANCEMENT

1) Read Judges 7:1-7.
2) Record, as a remainder, the number of men who did not return and were not afraid (10,000 men), and record, as a subtrahend, the number of men who were afraid and returned (22,000 men).
3) Calculate the total number of men Gideon started with.
4) Consider how God continued to reduce the number from 10,000 men (minuend) to merely 300 men (remainder) because no flesh is going to glory in God's presence.
5) Calculate the subtrahend.

EVIDENCE OF TEACHING SUCCESS

Every student was actively engaged in the lesson. They were able to do a similar problem on their slates.

EVIDENCE OF LEARNING SUCCESS

The next day, students were able to explain the subtraction strategy taught, and they were able to apply it to their homework successfully.

Tell • Explain **Mathematics Lesson Plan** Demonstrate • Inspire

Grade 5 Date 4/22/00 Quarter 4 Week 1 Teacher Mrs. Robinson Title A Biblical Lesson in Percentages

Component Numbers/Numeration & Notation/Operations/Problem Solving Math Skill(s) Calculate buyer's price with discount

Resources Webster's 1828 Dictionary; Ray's New Practical Arithmetic pp. 208-209; scissors; plain white paper; glue; merchant catalogs

Biblical References John 3:30; Lev. 27:30-32 Homework Clip employment ads and classifieds from daily newspaper, bring to school

PRINCIPLE(S) TAUGHT OR DEMONSTRATED ↓	The percentage of any number is the same part of that number as the given rate is of 100.
LEADING IDEA(S) ↓	The percent shows the change (up or down) relative to the original amount. "He must increase, but I must decrease." (John 3:30)
GOAL OF THE LESSON	The purpose of this lesson is to have the students learn how to calculate the selling price of an article when given a base and rate of discount.
TEACHER PRESENTATION: ↓	Introduce the purpose and goal of the lesson. This lesson teaches the percent discount from Ray's Article 173 pp. 208-209. Ask, "Do you like to shop?" "Do you like to find sales?" "How do you know if it is a good sale?"
REVIEW RELATED CONCEPT OR SKILL	Percentage and its vocabulary.
VOCABULARY	Use Webster's 1828 Dictionary to define: 1. price 3. rate of discount 2. base 4. discount
INSTRUCTION AND REASONING (Use the Five-Step Method)	**Problem:** If I see a book in a store with a regular price of $12.50 and the store offers a sale of 15% off, how much will I pay for the book? 1. Given: Regular price of book is $12.50 Discount of 15% 2. Find: The discounted price of the book 3. Analysis: 1. Express the rate 15% in decimals. 2. Calculate the discount by multiplying the base by the rate expressed decimally. 3. Subtract the discount (step 2 above) from the regular price to determine the discounted price. 4. Solution: 1. 15% = .15 2. $12.50 X .15 = $1.875 which rounds up to a discount amounting to $1.88. 3. $12.50 - $1.88 = $10.62 5. Check: Reverse operations in the solution steps above to verify arithmetic. **Summarize:** 1. Summarize the principles and terms of percentage through student interaction, and have students record in their notebooks notes you place on the board. 2. Review the lesson through teacher-directed oral quizzing of students. 3. Collect their activity papers and check them for accuracy. Return the papers to the students and have them make corrections as needed.

STUDENT INTERACTION AND REINFORCEMENT	***Student Practice:*** 1. Have students find four (4) different items with different prices in a merchandise catalog. 2. Cut out pictures of the items with their prices. 3. Glue the pictures onto a piece of paper. 4. Discount each item at a different rate (less than 50%). For example: 10%, 20%, 25%, and 30%. 5. On a separate paper, calculate the price to the buyer for each item. 6. On the paper with the pictures, write the % discount and the price to the buyer. ***Student Presentation:*** Have each student orally present his reasoning and evidence of his participation to the entire class.
LESSON ENHANCEMENT	***Biblical Example:*** **Ask students:** "What percent is one tenth? Let us look at what the Bible says about tithing." **Leviticus 27:30-32:** "A tithe of everything from the land, whether grain from the soil or fruit from the trees, belongs to the LORD; it is holy to the LORD. If a man redeems any of his tithe, he must add a fifth of the value to it. The entire tithe of the herd and flock—every tenth animal that passes under the shepherd's rod—will be holy to the LORD." **Define tithe:** The tenth part of any thing; but appropriately, the tenth part of the increase annually arising from the profits of land and stock, allotted to the clergy for their support. Tithes are personal, predial, or mixed: personal, when accruing from labor, art, trade, or navigation; predial, when issuing from the earth, as hay, wood, and fruit; and mixed, when accruing from animals, which are fed from the ground. **Problem:** If you earned $30 raking yards for your neighbors, what would your tithe be? ($3) How much would you have left over for your use? ($27) What operations are used to find these answers? (division and subtraction) **Homework:** Assign students to search the classified section of the daily newspaper and cut out employment advertisements that give hourly, weekly, monthly, or yearly rates of pay. Have them calculate the tithes on the amounts listed in the advertisements in class the next day.
EVIDENCE OF TEACHING SUCCESS	Every student was actively engaged in the lesson. They were able to do similar practice problems with success.
EVIDENCE OF LEARNING SUCCESS	Students' ability to solve correctly percentage problems using the Five-Step Method was evident when each shared his "best buy" with the rest of the class.

Tell • Explain **Mathematics Lesson Plan** Demonstrate • Inspire

Grade *Algebra 1* Date *4/22/00* Quarter *1* Week *8* Teacher *Mrs. Hunnewell* Title *Equations Requiring Two Transformations*

Component *Operations/Problem Solving* Math Skill(s) *Properties for transforming equations to solve for a given value*

Resources *Algebra 1, pp. 73–76; Bible; Webster's 1828 Dictionary*

Biblical References *1 Pet 1:15–16; Rom 12:2, 2 Cor 3:18* Homework *Text, p. 77, problems number 2–10 (even)*

PRINCIPLE(S) TAUGHT OR DEMONSTRATED

Addition Property of Equality: if $x = y$, then $x + z = y + z$
Multiplication Property of Equality: if $x = y$, then $xz = yz$

↓

LEADING IDEA(S)

Using these properties of equality involves transforming the given equation.
These transformations change the appearance of the equation, ultimately leading to the solution.
However, the equality value of the equation is never changed.
Because God is holy, He requires us to be transformed into His likeness.
These transformations do not change our value in Christ, but they do change our attitudes.

↓

GOAL OF THE LESSON

Teach students how to solve equations using transformations with the addition and multiplication properties of equality.

↓

TEACHER PRESENTATION:

REVIEW RELATED CONCEPT OR SKILL

Adding, subtracting, multiplying, and dividing signed numbers

VOCABULARY

transformation: to change the form, shape, or appearance of. In algebra, the change of an equation into one of a different form, but of equal value.

equality: an agreement of things in dimensions, quantity, or quality; likeness; similarity in regard to two things compared.

INSTRUCTION AND REASONING (Use the Five-Step Method)

Problem: Solve this equation using the addition and multiplication properties of equality:

1. *Given:* $\frac{1}{5}x + 4 = 13$

2. *Find:* The value of x that satisfies the equation

3. *Analysis:*
   a) Use the addition property of equality to add a -4 to both sides of the equation: $\frac{1}{5}x + 4 - 4 = 13 - 4$
   b) Combine like terms: $\frac{1}{5}x = 9$
   c) Use the multiplication property of equality to multiply both sides of the equation by 5. $(5)\frac{1}{5}x = 9(5)$
   d) Multiply: $x = 45$

4. *Solution:*
   a) $\frac{1}{5}x + 4 - 4 = 13 - 4$
   b) $\frac{1}{5}x = 9$
   c) $(5)\frac{1}{5}x = 9(5)$
   d) $x = 45$

5. *Check:* Substitute the calculated value of x into the original equation and solve. The resulting equality proves the value of x is correct.

$$(\tfrac{1}{5})(45) + 4 = 13$$
$$9 + 4 = 13$$
$$13 = 13$$

STUDENT INTERACTION AND REINFORCEMENT	*Assign the following practice problems to be solved on paper. Students should be prepared to present their reasoning and solutions orally.* 1) $5 - 3c = 17$ $5 - 3c - 5 = 17 - 5$ $-3c = 12$ $(-\frac{1}{3})(-3c) = 12(-\frac{1}{3})$ $c = -4$ 2) $\frac{3}{2}x + 4 = -9$ $\frac{3}{2}x + 4 - 4 = -9 - 4$ $\frac{3}{2}x = -13$ $(\frac{2}{3})\frac{3}{2}x = -13(\frac{2}{3})$ $x = -\frac{26}{3}$
LESSON ENHANCEMENT	*Word Problems in Algebra 1, pp. 82–3* *Bible: 1 Peter 1:13–16. Identify ways we Christians are transformed to be holy.*
EVIDENCE OF TEACHING SUCCESS	*Students actively engaged in the lesson.* *Lesson satisfied each learning style.*
EVIDENCE OF LEARNING SUCCESS	*Students successfully answered similar questions in class on the board.* *Students successfully completed homework assignment.*

Tell • Explain **Mathematics Lesson Plan** Demonstrate • Inspire

Grade *AP Calculus* Date *9/20/00* Quarter *1* Week *3* Teacher *Mr. Lindner* Title *The Case for Calculus*

Component *Numbers/Notation/Measurement/Problem Solving* Math Skill(s) *Finding the equation of a line that is tangent to the graph of some function at a specific point*

Resources *Calculus Text; Bible; Webster's 1828 Dictionary*

Biblical References *Psalm 147:5* Homework *None*

PRINCIPLE(S) TAUGHT OR DEMONSTRATED
The measuring of an instantaneous rate of change of a function's graph when change is not linear; i.e., A/C pulling Gs at a varying rate.

↓

LEADING IDEA(S)
God is boundless, infinite, and eternal. God has no limits. (See Psalm 147:5)

↓

GOAL OF THE LESSON
To demonstrate the need for calculus and make a connection between linear algebra and calculus.

↓

TEACHER PRESENTATION:

REVIEW RELATED CONCEPT OR SKILL
This introductory lesson does not require review.

VOCABULARY
limit: a boundary, utmost extent, confine; to restrain, to restrain from a lax or general significance.

INSTRUCTION AND REASONING (Use the Five-Step Method)
Show the movie clip "The Right Stuff" where John Glenn is re-entering the atmosphere. Discuss his approaching a "limit" and man's concept of a limit.

Problem: *Linear algebra cannot measure "instantaneous" rate of change*

1. **Given:** *The tangent line problem – **Limits** (our need for them)*
2. **Find:** *The equation of a line which is tangent to the graph of some function at a specific point*
3. **Analysis:** ***distance–velocity–acceleration:*** *all related by rate of change with respect to time*
   - *rate of change is normally measured with slope: "rise over run," but with nonlinear change, another method must be available*
   - *let us measure the slope of a line which approximates the curvature of a nonlinear graph/function*
   - *find the slope of this tangent line (touching the curve at a 90-degree angle at a point we will call P; this tangent line we call a secant line denoted by the letter l*

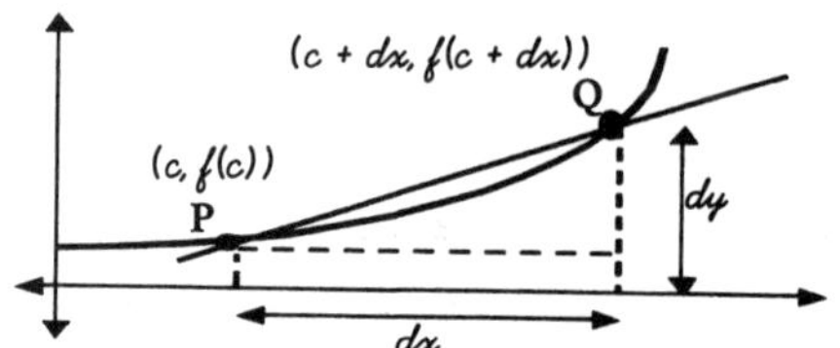

slope of the secant line = rise/run = $\frac{f(c+dx)-f(c)}{c+dx-c}$

   - *Now, to obtain a more accurate measure of a tangent line at point P, we could move Q closer to P, thereby decreasing dx and dy, and the secant line would become the tangent line. Q is said to approach P at a limiting position, and the slope of the tangent line is said to be the **Limit** of the slope of the secant line.*

4. **Solution:**
   - *Consider* $f(x) = \frac{x^3 - 1}{x - 1}$*, where x is not equal to 1. Let us explore the behavior of the function and its graph as x approaches 1 since we cannot define f(x) when x = 1. Let us approach x = 1 from both sides via a table as shown below:*

x	0.75	0.9	0.99	0.999	1	1.001	1.01	1.1	1.25
$f(x)$	2.313	2.71	2.97	2.997	undef	3.003	3.03	3.31	3.813

from the "left" f(x) approaches 3 *f(x) approaches 3 from the "right"*

- **Note:** although x cannot equal 1, we can get arbitrarily close to 1, an infinitely small "delta x," and thereby approach a limit.
- **Limit notation:**
  - $\lim_{x \to 1} f(x) = 3$, read "the limit of $f(x)$ as x approaches 1 is 3"
  - If any function $f(x)$ becomes arbitrarily close to a single number we call L as x approaches some value we call c from either side, then the limit of $f(x)$ as x approaches c is L denoted as follows:
    - $\lim_{x \to c} f(x) = L$

    Note: the existence of $f(x)$ at $x = c$ has no bearing on the existence of the limit of $f(x)$ as x approaches c.
- **Limits may fail to exist for a function** (differing behavior of $f(x)$ from the left and from the right).
  - Consider $f(x) = \frac{|x|}{x}$ and the limit of this function as x approaches 0
  - We know that for this function, x cannot be equal to 0. Therefore, let us approach 0 from the left and right with the aid of a graphing calculator and inspect the graph of $f(x)$ as shown below:

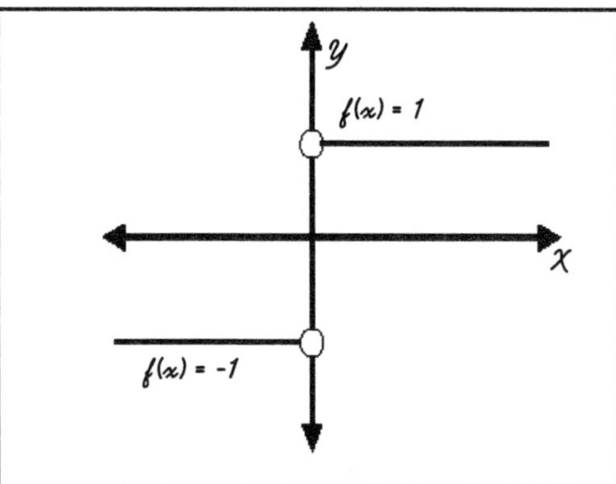

- Note in the above graph that when $x>0$, the $f(x) = 1$, and when $x<0$, the $f(x) = -1$, which are differing values of $f(x)$ as x approaches 0; therefore, **No limit exists** at $x = 0$.

5. **Check:** Use a graphing calculator to explore the behavior of a function as the domain approaches a limiting value.

STUDENT INTERACTION AND REINFORCEMENT

Students practice using a graphing calculator.

Have students orally present their reasoning and evidence of participation to the teacher and class.

LESSON ENHANCEMENT

Biblical example of calculus and limits: "And David put his hand in his bag, and took thence a stone, and slang it, and smote the Philistine in his forehead, that the stone sunk into his forehead; and he fell upon his face to the earth." (1 Samuel 17:49) In this well-known passage of David and Goliath, David unknowingly applied the concept in calculus of limits leading into derivatives. While the stones were being slung, they were experiencing acceleration that was not linear. From the laws of physics and employing calculus, we now know that acceleration is the first derivative of velocity with respect to time that could be computed by taking the limit of the velocity as the change in time approached zero. This allows us to compute an instantaneous rate of change for a nonlinear function.

EVIDENCE OF TEACHING SUCCESS

Participation and attention.

Quality of student questions.

EVIDENCE OF LEARNING SUCCESS

Homework accuracy. Students' ability to solve correctly similar problems using calculus.

Formal assessment, accuracy, and performance.

Notes

The Notebook Method

The Notebook Method is the tool of reasoning and academic discipline found in the Principle Approach® and most consistently in the education of men and women of great historic character. It requires both teacher and student to make a written copy of their studies. See pages 25–32 in *The Noah Plan® Self-Directed Study (NPSDS)* for a complete description of the underlying philosophy and the four basic steps of learning: research, reason, relate, and record. With practice, when incorporated and balanced in the study of mathematics, the 4-R's will produce the following qualities:

1. Reflective thinking and reasoning
2. Mastery of the discipline or principle
3. Ability to speak and write with authority and perspicuity
4. Self-governing character
5. Independent learning habits
6. Standard of Christian scholarship
7. Permanent record of progress and learning for further study and reflection

The proper use of the Notebook Method by the teacher serves as an important tool to govern the study of mathematics. Most mathematics curricula are written from a secular philosophy and methodology and include a teacher manual with daily teacher lesson plans and consumable student workbooks. Schools spend thousands of dollars each year to provide these consumable workbooks for their students. Quite often, a "canned curriculum" does not require mastery of subject nor full comprehension of the principles for the teacher to teach the subject. Additionally, students spend endless hours filling in workbook blanks and reviewing the same material over and over again. Time spent in excessive review of concepts already mastered does not produce comprehension. When students truly comprehend the material, this decreases the need for review; whereas, skills and concepts learned by rote require frequent practice to be applied. The Notebook Method teaches students the art of learning! The art of learning requires both teacher and students to think, reflect, and reason with principles and concepts in order to fully comprehend and master the discipline.

The Notebook Method requires the teacher to prepare lesson plans beginning with principles and leading ideas in a concise manner. Most math textbooks can be utilized. The teacher simply adjusts the method by which the lesson is imparted and employs the 4-R's to teaching and learning. The Biblical foundation is laid for each lesson plan and the lesson is imparted to the student beginning with the principle, concept, or leading idea. In the elementary classroom, students learn to record simple notes from the chalkboard written by the teacher, which provide a written record for study and review. Sample problems are recorded for reference and study. The discipline being taught is placed on the Chain of Christianity® and its Gospel purpose taught, as well as a small biographical sketch of a mathematician. All homework, quizzes, and exams are filed in the students' notebooks.

Notebook Standard

The Notebook Standard of Form is taught at the beginning of every year and is reinforced by the teacher daily. Sturdy, plain-colored, three-ring binders are used. It is recommended that mathematics and science be placed in the same binder. The binder's spine is labeled with the names of the subjects and the student. Students are taught how to steward their notebooks with care to reflect the standard of Christian scholarship taught. The Notebook Standard of Form requires that the notebook be neat, accurate, complete, and in correct order, with pages reinforced if necessary. All lines must be ruled; one color ink used throughout; colored pencils used for any illustrations. Each page of notes should be headed at the top with the date and numbered in sequence for filing purposes.

Notes

Each student notebook is graded quarterly by the teacher to encourage the standard and habit of scholarship taught. The grade represents 25% of the final grade. In the elementary and middle levels of learning (K–8), the teacher should spend time before the grading period assisting students in preparing their notebooks for grading. The purpose is to enable every student to be successful in his notebook work and to be proud of his labor. See sample student notebook work, *NPMG*, pages 159–176.

Student Notebook Setup

1. **Mathematics Title Page**

   Just as every book has a title and a copyright page, the student's notebook should reflect similar information. See *NPSDS*, page 34 for an example.

2. **Classroom Constitution**

   See *NPSDS*, pages 34 and 36 for placement and an example.

3. **Mathematics Grade-Level or Branch Overview**

   Insert the curriculum chart for the grade level or branch of mathematics being taught from chapter one of this guide, *NPMG*, pages 17–43.

4. **Mathematics Dividers Marked**

   Foundations to include Biblical principles, philosophy, and principles of the program or branch of mathematics

   His Story of Math to include a Mathematics Christian History Timeline, which each student creates as mathematics is taught on the Chain of Christianity®

   Vocabulary

   Numeration and Notation

   Operations

   Homework

   Quizzes and Tests

Suggested Dividers for *RightStart*™ and *Ray's*™

***RightStart*™ Program** (grades K–4)

- Foundations
- His Story of Math
- Vocabulary
- Arithmetic
- Homework Worksheets
- Practice Sheets
- Review Sheets/Tests

Ray's*™ *Arithmetics (grades 5–7)

- Foundations
- His Story of Math
- Key Word Definitions
- Numeration and Notation
- Operations
- Fractions
- Compound Denominate Numbers
- Ratio/Proportion
- Percentage
- Average
- Exponents
- Roots
- Geometry/Graphing
- Glossary
- Quizzes/Tests
- Homework

Other dividers with tabs will be necessary for Algebra through Calculus.

Preparing to Teach Mathematics

Your personal research and written record should be organized in such a way that it will enable you to teach any age group of students. Compile your research in sturdy three-ring binders with dividers that reflect the whole subject. This will help you locate your research quickly, add to your record, and enable you to teach the subject at any time.

Notes

Teacher Notebook Setup

1. Label a three-ring binder "Mathematics."
2. Create a title page.
3. Insert the chart for the grade-level or branch of mathematics that you are teaching, (located in chapter one, *NPMG*, pages 17–43).
4. Create Dividers labeled:
   Foundations
   His Story of Math
   Vocabulary
   Grade-Level Overviews
   Methods
   Resources
   Bibliography
   Sample Student Work

Preparation

1. Read thoroughly the chart "Developing Subject Curriculum in the Principle Approach®" in chapter one, *NPMG*, pages 80–81.
2. Study the mathematics curriculum chart for the grade level or discipline chosen (*NPMG*, 17–43).
3. Define the vocabulary and complete any key word studies as needed (see *NPSDS*, 23–27).
4. Four-R the Biblical principles and the principles within the discipline. Identify leading ideas.
5. Research and develop biographical sketches for mathematicians and disciplines on the Chain of Christianity®. See *NPMG*, page 136, in the Appendix for an example.
6. Develop your Christian History Mathematics Timeline for your discipline.
7. Gather enrichment resources, tools, and bulletin board ideas to enhance your curriculum.
8. Maintain a bibliography.
9. See *NPMG*, pages 86–97, for lesson plan format and lesson plan examples.

Teaching Mathematics

The Teacher

This Biblical and classical approach to teaching and learning is that a knowledgeable teacher introduces a new mathematical principle, explains what it is, shows how it works, and then assigns problems for students to solve using this new information. Through much practice, students deepen their understanding and accumulate fundamental skills successfully. The teacher requires students to commit basic vocabulary, facts, and formulas to memory by using the information regularly and recording it in the student notebook. Partial credit is often given for using reasonable methods to solve test problems.

Teachers are expected to impart systematically the knowledge they possess and guide students through the deductive reasoning of mathematics. Practical applications are included with theoretical problem solving. Mathematics is a structured body of knowledge and must be taught by teachers who impart their mathematical knowledge directly in a "precept upon precept; line upon line" (Isaiah 28:10) method of instruction using a variety of proven techniques that appeal to all learning styles. Activities for learning are very helpful when the mathematics teacher has taught and explained the concept. Mathematics should be enjoyable and challenging. The use of games enhances learning, but should not replace mathematical understanding. Practical applications of mathematics must be part of the mathematics curriculum but should not replace problems and skills that deal with abstractions. Mathematics develops the students' ability to think and reason clearly, exactly, and in an orderly manner, and encourages an independence of thought.

The Student

Learning mathematics involves building a mental reserve of rules, terms, axioms, and theorems by which the subject is mastered. This is true for any subject, especially language. In order to recall words or facts, the student is required to communicate an exact idea. So, too, in mathematics. Doing well in math requires the accurate recall of basic information.

It must always be there ready to be used when needed. This mental reserve of math facts begins in the first grade and should be mastered by fourth grade.

Practice

All students must practice math in order to learn it. Regular practice with understanding causes the learner to enjoy mathematics, because it makes him successful. This success is guaranteed to the learner because, like God, mathematics is reliable. A teacher may commit a whole class period to a single problem because he wants the children to develop a deep understanding of the ideas at work.

Mechanical Calculating Tools

The use of tools in computation is acknowledged as an economic benefit to man. The history of computation and calculating machines spans the use of the abacus in ancient civilizations to the modern computer. Various calculating machines have been used routinely in the marketplace and in the sciences throughout history. The efficient use of these tools has always depended upon first knowing the principles of computation and mastering mental math before relying on the tool and replacing mental math. When the operations are fully learned and mastered, then calculators can be introduced. Basic mathematical calculations may be done mentally when mastery is achieved. Daily practice keeps math skills finely honed.

The Closure Principle

The one correct answer is important. As the truth of the statement, "Ideas have consequences" is incontrovertible, so, too, is the statement, "Correct answers matter." Mathematics is an exact discipline and requires accuracy in thinking, procedures, computation, notation, and adjudication to arrive at the correct answer. Correct answers computed by engineers are what keep our bridges, dams, and buildings from collapsing. Correct answers are what transport us from point *a* to point *b* when navigating our jet planes, boats, and automobiles. Correct answers are what propel our astronauts to and from the moon. One can only begin to imagine the devastating effects incorrect answers have on our everyday lives. Students must be trained that correct answers matter in mathematics.

Teaching Arithmetic

Qualifications

The chief qualifications for successful teaching:

1. A mastery and love of the subject
2. An aptitude to teach

Tools

1. The white board and numerical frame (American abacus) are indispensable to the primary school teacher. Demonstrating the solution on the board, so that all may see while you are instructing, helps students understand it at once. To illustrate the increase or decrease of numbers, the process of adding, subtracting, multiplying, and dividing on the numerical frame furnishes the simplest and most convenient method of instruction.
2. Student mathematics notebook:
   It is essential for the student to record his reasoning, demonstrations, rules, principles, and examples in his notebook.

Analysis and Reason

Analyze every problem and reason every step in the solution until this process becomes a habit with each student.

Objects of the Study

1. Discipline of the mind and development of the reasoning powers
2. Facility and accuracy in the application of numbers to business calculations

Character Qualities

1. Thoroughness:
   - Review
   - Prove every operation
   - Perform practical exercises
   - Reason from examples under a rule and principle
   - Present an accurate account of the solution and give a reason for each step in one's own words or those of the author
   - Daily mental arithmetic throughout the whole course is very useful in producing accurate arithmeticians

Notes

This year I've learned the most about fractions and decimals. Before I came to this school, I didn't know anything about decimals. It was fun to learn how to add, subtract, multiply, and divide them. I've gained confidence in using decimals and fractions! I can't wait to learn more and keep gaining knowledge from this school next year. And when I'm an adult, I'll look back on this experience and smile, and think how much I learned there.

Ethan R.
Sixth Grade
StoneBridge School
Chesapeake, Virginia

Notes

2. Self-reliance:
   - When students require assistance, it should be given indirectly by explaining the meaning of the question or illustrating the principle on which the operation depends by referring to a familiar case. This enables the student to solve the problem or question himself.
   - Students should always be encouraged to think, reason, and even struggle to solve problems themselves before answers are provided. It is very helpful for students to see how others have solved the problem and agree that there may be many approaches to solving a given problem. Students should always select the one most concise arithmetical solution.
   - Students should be encouraged to master the art of computation and learn to solve problems independently of having an answer key. Without this independent attainment, the disciplines of scholarship and growth in confidence are not achieved.

May your life be like arithmetic:
joys added,
sorrows substracted,
friends multiplied,
love undivided.
(unknown)

Notes

Teaching Mathematics as a Language

Without the knowledge of the patterns of God's speech in the creation, you are powerless to replenish the earth and will instead be subdued by it. Now it is true that the melody of nature's song can be enjoyed without a knowledge of the underlying mathematical structure, . . . but the lyric of the "music of the spheres" is mathematics.

(Larry Zimmerman, 1980)

A mathematics curriculum taught by a skillful and inspired Christian mathematician will communicate the internal, external, and eternal purposes and value of mathematics to the mind and heart of the student. With a rich and inspired curriculum, students retain ideas for long periods of time and reason with accumulated mathematical knowledge without meaningless and endless review of previously taught material. This view of curriculum frees the teacher and student to delve deeply into mathematical ideas that reveal the majesty and excellence of the attributes of God's nature and character as they are seen in the physical creation and make application to all of life and learning. Students who are required to learn meaningless ideas and procedures in rote-based curricula forget them easily and, therefore, these ideas must be painfully taught year after year. One of the major consequences of rote-based teaching and learning is the pressure teachers feel to cover huge amounts of material at breakneck speeds.

In the late 1700s through the 1800s, the beginning student of arithmetic was actively led through mental and oral work. There was a minimum of writing and a maximum of thinking. This approach trained minds to *do* and *apply* mathematics without the hindrance of pencil and paper. During that era, educators recognized the limitations of the learner, yet they realized that mathematical principles are *demonstrable*. Therefore, they taught beginners by (1) demonstrating the principles of mathematics; (2) employing the vocabulary of the subject; (3) requiring mental effort, not talent, to solve the problems; (4) using very few manipulative tools; and (5) introducing abstract symbols and signs to the learner. This comprehensive approach developed a strong foundation in mathematics that served the learner for an entire lifetime.

Mathematics Is the Language of Science

It is well known and generally accepted that mathematics is the language of science. Johannes Kepler, the renowned sixteenth-century scientist and mathematician, stated, "The chief aim of all investigations of the external world should be to discover the rational order and harmony which has been imposed on it by God and which he revealed to us in the language of mathematics."[1] When mathematics is understood to be a language, it can be taught at a very young age. "Man's propensity for language acquisition and development begins immediately after birth. It accelerates in the second year in function and vocabulary, and is refined and expanded at ages three and four. Language development continues through adolescence."[2]

When mathematics is understood to be a language, it can be taught at a very young age.

When a young child is playing with his blocks, it is simple for him to see only one block, and then see two blocks. Parents quite naturally teach the child to say, "one" and "two," pointing to the blocks as they are counted. Yet, it would be laughable to any observer if the parent also handed that same child a pencil and a piece of paper and began to write and say the abstract symbols 1+1 = 2. It is easy to reason that the language stage of teaching mathematics precedes the written stage. The language and the manipulation stages of learning occur simultaneously. Any object qualifies as a manipulative—crayons, buttons, books, shoes, trees, etc. During the oral/manipulative stage, a child learns to speak and mentally connect speech to objects before developing the ability to write. This is teaching arithmetic, its vocabulary, numbers, and operations, and it does not require the learner to know how

1 Johannes Kepler, *Astronomis Nova de Motibus . . .*, 1609.

2 E. Polloway and T. Smith, *Language Instruction for Students with Disabilities*, 2nd Ed. Denver, CO: Love Publishing Co., 1992, 27.

Notes

to write. Maximize the teaching and learning of mathematics during this stage by doing it orally and mentally. Later, when the child is learning to encode and decode the alphabet, he can also learn to encode and decode numerals with numbers. He then encodes the language previously learned into symbolic characters, and learns to decode them, too. Teaching one to encode and decode prematurely interferes with the process of language development in the learner. Introducing the writing of numbers prematurely often results in distracting the learner from gaining understanding and shifting his energy to the proper mechanics or the proper location of symbols on the page. It undermines the learner's ability and capacity to think mathematically during all later stages of his mathematical life.

Speak the language of mathematics to the young child and he will learn to speak and think mathematically. The very young child learns to speak and think in English because he hears English spoken by those around him. A child learns a language by imitation first, not by instruction in the principles of grammar. Mathematics is a language and, as such, must be taught at a time when language development is strongest in the child.

Next, the child will convert his knowledge with real objects into mental images as he thinks about them. Once the learner realizes this is a faster way to work, he naturally abandons the use of objects. He does so because he has internalized his thinking and is able to do the work mentally without external hindrances. This results in liberty for the individual! A child who has not become dependent upon written mathematics is well beyond others his age, because he is developing the ability to think independently. (If you cannot add three numbers in rapid succession mentally, but seek to use paper and pencil for the exercise, then you are a casualty of the method of teaching mathematics that produced students who could not think mathematically.)

Finally, as the child internalizes knowledge and applies it in unfamiliar situations, his recorded and written solutions become appropriate. Knowing how to write (encode) is as much an element of language as listening and comprehending the spoken element of language. Teaching students where and how to write computations should not be confused for understanding it. It is during this last stage of mathematical development that the principles and rules of arithmetic are mastered and the applications practiced patiently. A student following this sequence is able to "think mathematically": (1) language; (2) mental; (3) abstract to mathematics. To think mathematically, the student has mastered the art of computation and the science of numbers and is able to solve problems to the benefit of mankind and the glory of God. Such a person understands what he knows, why it is true, and how to apply his understanding to problem solving.

Universal Principles Expressed in the Language of Mathematics

Principle (Cause)	Commutative (Addition)	Associative (Addition)	Commutative (Multiplication)	Associative (Multiplication)	Distributive
Rule (Effect)	Two like numbers may be added in any order without altering the sum.	Several like numbers may be added in any combination without altering the sum.	Two numbers may be multiplied in either order without altering the product.	Several numbers may be multiplied in any order or combination without altering the product.	When a number multiplies a sum, the result is the same as the sum of the separate products of the multiplier and each addend.
Formula (Effect)	$a + b = b + a$	$a+(b+c)=(a+b)+c$	$a \cdot b = b \cdot a$	$a \cdot (b \cdot c) = (a \cdot b) \cdot c$	$a(b+c)=(a \cdot b)+(a \cdot c)$
Example (Effect)	$1 + 2 = 2 + 1$ $3 = 3$	$1 + (2+3) = (1+2) + 3$ $1 + 5 = 3 + 3$ $6 = 6$	$1 \cdot 2 = 2 \cdot 1$ $2 = 2$	$1 \cdot (2 \cdot 3) = (1 \cdot 2) \cdot 3$ $1 \cdot 6 = 2 \cdot 3$ $6 = 6$	$1(2 + 3) = (1 \cdot 2) + (1 \cdot 3)$ $1 \cdot 5 = 2 + 3$ $5 = 5$

Notes

Comparison of English Language to Mathematics

English Language Components	Mathematics Components
Etymology Origins of words Word analysis	**Numbers** Origins of numbers Number analysis: the characteristics of numbers
Orthography Spelling (encoding) Alphabetic characters (26)	**Notation** Notation: writing numerals using symbols to communicate ideas (encoding) Numerical characters and symbols; the science of numbers
Prosody Poetry Melody Literature as art	**Measurement** Mathematics has as its poetry the equation! It states truth with precision, conveys volumes of information in brief terms, and often is difficult for the uninitiated to comprehend. The equation enables us to see far beyond ourselves.[2]
Syntax Sentence analysis/synthesis Word order (N – V – dO) Syntactical government	**Operations** Problem solving (Five-Step Method); place value Order of operations; orderly arrangement of numbers on the number line Operations govern the language of mathematics
Composition Lost art of language	**Problem Solving** The art of mental and manual computation Applying mathematics to life in practical ways

Mathematics is the language of science and must be taught as a language. "Ever since the seventeenth century, when Newton . . . invented the calculus, *mathematics* . . . [has been] the chosen language of science. . . . Even when written flawlessly, any ordinary language—English, Latin, Greek—could be misunderstood as much as 20 percent of the time. By contrast, mathematics appeared to be the only form of communication with which natural philosophers could hope to describe the world with perfect clarity."[3] Mathematics class is an ideal place to learn, discuss, and explain one's thinking, as well as to listen to others and how they think. As a language, informal mathematics precedes paper and pencil work just as normal speaking skills are first developed informally. As a language, a mathematical problem is an interrogatory sentence put forward for analyzing, solving, and validating. Therefore, teachers and students must not be too eager to give away the solution (property) to the problem before others have had an opportunity to grapple with the problem and solve it.

It is well-documented that Asian students surpass American students by the middle of the first grade and the gap widens every year thereafter.[4] In the United States of America, half the children in fourth grade are still learning place value concepts.[5] Asian children develop this concept years sooner. Why? One answer offered by Dr. Joan Cotter is that the Asian student has a philosophy of teaching and learning that believes in effort by the student

2 M. Guillen, *Five Equations that Changed the World*. New York: Hyperion, 1995, 2.

3 Ibid., 157.

4 The Third International Mathematics and Science Study (TIMSS) A study conducted in 1994–95 by the U.S. National Research Center and the Dept. of Education, in which 4th, 8th, and 12th graders of 41 countries were tested and evaluated to determine who was first in the world in mathematics and science achievement. On average, U.S. students scored 38th in math and science.

5 Based on studies by Kamii, 1985; Ross, 1989; Muira and Okamoto, 1989, cited by Joan A. Cotter, PH.D., in "Using Language and Visualization to Teach Place," *Teaching Children Mathematics*, Vol. 7, No. 2, October, 2000. Reston, VA: National Council of Teachers of Mathematics.

Notes

Teaching and Learning the Language of Mathematics

Phase of Instruction	Grade Level	Emphasized Instructional Mode
The art of computation	K–Grade 1	Oral, visual, auditory, and kinesthetic development
	Grades 2–4	Mental and written development
The science of numbers	Grades 5–7	Proficiency moving toward mastery of arithmetic business applications
	Grades 8–12	Higher branches of mathematics practically applied (algebra, geometry, trigonometry, calculus)

and good instruction by the teacher.[6] It is not based on natural talent but effort. This work ethic is what determines a student's success in mathematics, which is the same one disparagingly referred to as the "Puritanical ethic"—hard work and effort—that contributed to making America great!

What solutions can be applied to the teaching and learning of mathematics that would solve this growing problem in American mathematics education? First, the linguistic nature of mathematics must be recognized and regular *value-number naming* must be implemented. Secondly, mathematics must be taught in a way that produces *mental imaging of quantities* rather than unitary counting. Thirdly, *the quantities of manipulative tools used to teach mathematics must be reduced* and thereby eliminate confusion.

Forming Mathematical Thinkers through the Grades

Teaching mathematics is both a challenge and an honor. Training challenges the reading or English teacher in the same way. As the English teacher equips students with linguistic skills, the mathematics teacher equips students with mathematical skills and the ability to think mathematically, or mathematical and quantitative scholarship. The test for thinking mathematically is whether a person naturally defers to mathematical skills in other contexts, as opposed to compartmentalization, where skills or ideas learned in one class are totally forgotten when they arise in a different context. Many mathematicians today cannot apply theorems to science and technology precisely because they compartmentalize.

What Does It Mean to Think Mathematically?

Thinking mathematically extends beyond mere basic skills, elementary statistics, logical reasoning, and advanced mathematics. Thinking mathematically nurtures the entire school curriculum including the natural and applied sciences, as well as language, history, and the fine arts. It goes beyond the basic mathematical skills including arithmetic, percentages, ratios, simple algebra, measurement, estimation, logic, and geometric reasoning. It embraces estimating tolerances and error, simulating complex systems on computers, using flowcharts for planning and management. This draws Biblical, statistical, scientific, and logical inferences appropriately and presents data-based arguments by using computer tools, as well as thinking, visualizing and calculating in three dimensions. This should be taught across the curriculum.

Thinking mathematically is another foundation block in a solid education. Building that foundation

[6] Based on studies by Kamii, 1985; Ross, 1989; Muira and Okamoto, 1989, cited by Joan A. Cotter, PH.D., in "Using Language and Visualization to Teach Place," *Teaching Children Mathematics*, Vol. 7, No. 2, October, 2000. Reston, VA: National Council of Teachers of Mathematics.

Notes

block into the education of our children begins in kindergarten and continues diligently throughout high school. The components of mathematics presented in this guide work within the context of the entire school curriculum and draw upon the teaching of Bible, history, science, and other languages to create a unique, distinct, and complete view of mathematics. Teachers must encourage students to see and use mathematics in everything they do: measurement in science; logic and reasoning in language; ratios and rhythms in music; geometry in art; scoring and ranking in athletics; and reading maps.

For centuries, verbal literacy has been recognized as a free citizen's best insurance against ignorance and society's best bulwark against tyranny. In colonial America, such leaders as Benjamin Franklin and Thomas Jefferson promoted and demonstrated mathematical thinking to support the new republic. So today, in the age of information and statistical data, the goal is to join quantitative literacy with verbal literacy as the guarantor of liberty for the individual and society. Christian educators must promote thinking mathematically to support and sustain our American Christian constitutional republic and our heritage of "liberty for all."

Value-Number Naming

Value-number naming is one of the factors associated with the high mathematical achievement of Asian American students (Miura and Okamoto, 1989).[7] Some Asian languages say "two-ten three" when speaking the symbols 23. Visualizing a quantity of two-tens is much less complex than imagining twenty-three units. In English the quantity ten is linguistically communicated in three ways: *ten*, *-teen* (i.e., six*teen*), and *-ty* (i.e. thir*ty*). Eleven and twelve seem to make no sense where as "one-ten one," describes a quantity clearly—one ten and one unit. Similarly, "one-ten two" is understood clearly and indicates the proper place value associated with computation. Sixteen, for example, reverses place-value. The order is reversed with the units *six ones* stated before the *ten*, violating the principle of local value.

Asian American students scored higher in mathematics than other groups. Asian American third graders who spoke only English scored in the 54th percentile, while students who were also fluent in Chinese or Japanese scored in the 99th percentile and 97th percentile. This contrasts with bilingual Spanish-speaking third grade students who scored in the 16th percentile, proving these results to be linguistically, not genetically, relevant.[8]

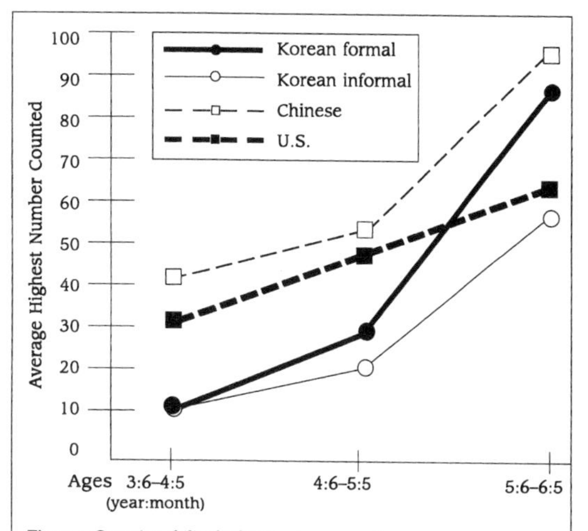

Figure 1. Counting ability by language.
M. Song, and H. Ginsburg, "The effect of the Korean number system on young children's counting: natural experiment in numerical bilingualism." *International Journal of Psychology*, 23, 1988, 326.

Mental Imaging versus Counting

In Asia counting is discouraged. Students are taught to recognize and visualize quantities in fives and tens. The manipulative tools used are few and all cause visualization. All manipulative tools cause confusion at first because they require the student to go through learning how to use them. A good manipulative tool causes understanding, and when consistently used, it enhances learning better than using many different ones. Regular and consistent use of one tool reduces anxiety and confusion, which inhibit learning.

Most of the manipulative tools used in America cause confusion and distraction. Currently in America, counting is the basis of arithmetic and students are

7 Based on studies by Kamii, 1985; Ross, 1989; Muira and Okamoto, 1989, cited by Joan A. Cotter, PH.D., in "Using Language and Visualization to Teach Place," *Teaching Children Mathematics*, Vol. 7, No. 2, October, 2000. Reston, VA: National Council of Teachers of Mathematics.

8 Ibid.

Notes

taught to engage in counting strategies: forward and backward. Counting is very error-prone. Simply think of what businessmen go through when they attempt to inventory their supplies—counting starts and errors arise. Additionally, counting ignores place value, requires memorization of facts, and is inefficient and time-consuming.

Different philosophies of mathematics education produce different results. The view embracing mental imaging develops the art of computation by making principles demonstrable—upholding local-value (unity with diversity). It concurs with Noah Webster's definition of *mathematics* as "the science of quantity" and concurs with Dr. Joseph Ray's approach to the teaching and learning of mathematics in his texts first published in 1863.

Embracing mental imaging develops the art of computation by making principles demonstrable.

Present-day American Christian teachers must restore what has been lost through forgetfulness. We must rise to the challenge of restoring what once was in America. Let us remember the purpose of teaching mathematics, among other things, is to enable children to think mathematically and aid in the development of Christian character, not operate from rote. Let us remember that mathematics offers special opportunities for children to learn the power of thought based upon Biblical principles, distinct from merely the power of authority—"It is because I say so." Let us remember that when learning it is natural to make errors. The "effort causes learning" view treats errors made by students and teachers as natural to the realm of learning; hence, they can be and are discussed openly with all who want to learn from the error. In the "natural talent view" of learning mathematics, however, errors are a sign of personal failure and are to be avoided at any cost. The American Christian approach embraces the idea that effort causes learning. As such, let's teach the subject in ways that cause the student to love mathematics, and restore the base-ten (subbase-five) approach to numbers rather than a unitary concept, and let us meet the learning needs of all learners and learning modalities.

AL™—The American Abacus

AL, the abacus developed by engineer Dr. Joan Cotter, is an American abacus, not a Japanese or Chinese abacus. It is a simplified abacus that upholds all the principles of arithmetic without the complexity of an Asian abacus. Asian children do not start working with the Asian abacus until third grade. It is no longer part of the curriculum in Japan, where students use calculators. The use of the Asian abacus has been discontinued in Japan's schools because it takes many hours of practice to become proficient—time better spent learning other mathematics. The purpose of the Asian abacus is to perform calculations, not teach mathematics. Although addition and subtraction are faster for a master on the Japanese abacus compared to a calculator, multiplication, division, and square roots are slower.

The *AL* abacus was designed for different purposes. It is a hands-on, visual tool for young children to learn about quantity, place value, the four arithmetic operations, and efficient strategies for mastering math facts. Children as young as age four can use it successfully. Children gradually stop using it as they construct the representations and operations in their own minds.

Why Colored Rods Don't Work for Young Children

There are drawbacks for teaching with rods:

1. Young children think each rod is equivalent to the unit "one."
2. One out of twelve children have some color deficiency and cannot distinguish the ten colors needed to quickly identify the different rods. Even children who can detect colors normally may take a long time to learn the color scheme. The *AL Abacus* has only two very distinct colors.
3. Quantities over five are not imaginable unless grouped. For a child to reach the abstract stage, a concept must be imaginable or can be visualized.
4. Combining rods does not give the immediate sum.
5. Rods are not truly ten-based and do not teach ten-based place value.
6. Because of the many small pieces involved, rods are hard to manage, especially for children with learning challenges.

Notes

A Case against Incremental Learning

According to the Saxon Math literature, "At its simplest, incremental development is the introduction of topics in easily understandable pieces (increments), permitting the assimilation of one facet of a concept before the next facet is introduced. Both facets are then practiced together until another is introduced. The incrementalization of topics is combined with continual review, wherein all previously learned material is reviewed in every lesson for the entire year. Topics are never dropped but are instead increased in complexity and practiced every day, providing the time required for concepts to become totally familiar."[9]

The incremental theory initially sounds good, but it is based on misconceptions about the nature of human learning and the nature of mathematics. The incremental development theory of learning originated from the stimulus-response behaviorists Skinner and Watson. They assumed the individual was a passive learner who responded to a stimulus in a predictable manner. This theory resulted in some educators believing that if they broke learning concepts into small bite-sized pieces (spoon-feeding), the learner would be able to master the concept. However, the learner often misses the coherence of the whole concept, because the whole was not first presented to him. Teaching from whole-to-parts was changed to part-to-part, omitting the whole. A person possessing the skills of a discipline without understanding its principles and purpose remains incompetent. To understand and appreciate mathematics, students must use thinking and reasoning skills, including problem solving, modeling, applying, proving, justifying, and communicating; otherwise mathematics is meaningless and void of practical applications. Understanding principles of mathematics and knowing how to apply them to unfamiliar situations are what makes one a mathematician.

Students need to spend time thinking mathematically in order to understand mathematics. Time spent in excessive review is time not spent learning new mathematics. Real understanding decreases the need for review; whereas, skills learned by rote need to be maintained by frequent practice. Consider teaching parts of speech and reviewing it for twelve years. Just as we teach students to use the written word for further learning, we need to teach them to employ the language of mathematics to solve scientific and other problems in life. This will fulfill God's purpose in His ordained destiny for the individual. Let's spend more time on fewer problems of greater quality, teaching the language of mathematics with each occurrence.

[9] William J. Bennett, U.S. Secretary of Education, *James Madison High School—A Curriculum for American Students.* Washington, DC: U.S. Department of Education, December, 1987, 26.

All life is biology.

All biology is physiology.

All physiology is chemistry.

All chemistry is physics.

All physics is math.

(Dr. Stephen Marquarde)

Math is the language of science.

The Five-Step Method to Problem Solving

Step	Description	Relationship to 4-R'ing
1. Given	Record pertinent data correctly and completely as given in the word problem. Hint: Label all concrete numbers with the given unit of measure.	Research Reason Record
2. Find	Identify and record in a logical and orderly way what is required of the problem solver for the problem to be considered mathematically solved. Hint: Assign names to variables.	Research Reason Relate Record
3. Analysis *(Legislative)*	Compose and record a mathematically lawful, logical, and orderly plan in words that describe a possible solution to the problem using the language of mathematics. Hint: Use the language of mathematics for rules and principles of the subject in a properly sequenced order.	Research Reason Relate Record
4. Solution *(Executive)*	Execute the plan mathematically as described in the analysis section above. Work the plan! Hint: Execute the written plan. Keep your word. If incorrect, rectify the plan and keep it. "When the solution is simple, God is answering." (Albert Einstein)	Reason Record
5. Check *(Judicial)*	Verify the results against the requirements of the problem to determine if it is solved correctly. If not, correct the plan and its execution to arrive at the correct answer. Hint: Evaluate your own work before others do. Is the answer reasonable and does it make sense?	Research Reason Relate Record

The Five-Step Method to Problem Solving

Sample Arithmetic Homework Assignment for Seventh Grade

Problem: A college student has an income of \$1,200 a year. He spends 23% of it for room and board; $10\frac{2}{5}$% for clothing; $6\frac{3}{4}$% for books; $\frac{7}{12}$% for subscriptions; $12\frac{7}{8}$% on miscellaneous expenses; he saves the rest of his money: (A) How much does he pay for each item, and (B) How much does he save at the end of the year?

Step 1 Given: \$1,200 income; 23% room and board expense; $10\frac{2}{5}$% clothing expense; $6\frac{3}{4}$% book expense; $\frac{7}{12}$% subscription expense; $12\frac{7}{8}$% miscellaneous expense.

Step 2 Find:

A. How much does the student pay for each item in dollars?

B. How much does the student save at the end of the year?

Step 3 Analysis:

A1. Express the given rates (percentages) decimally.

A2. Calculate the dollar value of each item using the formula
P = B x R where P is the percentage, B is the base, and R is the rate.

B1. Add the calculated expenses in step A2 to obtain the total dollar amount spent on expenses.

B2. Subtract the total expenses from the annual income to determine the amount saved for the year.

Step 4 Solution:

A1. 23% = $\frac{23}{100}$ = 23; $10\frac{2}{5}$% = .104; $6\frac{3}{4}$% = .0675; $\frac{7}{12}$% = .0058; $12\frac{7}{8}$% = .12875.

A2.
\$1,200 x .23 = \$276.00 room and board
\$1,200 x .104 = \$124.80 clothing
\$1,200 x .0675 = \$ 81.00 books
\$1,200 x .0058 = \$ 6.96 subscriptions
\$1,200 x .12875 = \$154.50 miscellaneous

B1.
\$ 276.00 room and board
124.80 clothing
81.00 books
6.96 subscriptions
+ 134.50 miscellaneous
\$ 643.26 Total Expenses

B2.
\$1,200.00 Annual Income
\- 643.26 Annual Expenses
\$ 556.74 Annual Savings

Step 5 Check:

Example: Check A2
Divide to check multiplication; hence $\frac{\$276}{\$1,200}$ = .23. (Since the answer matches the one above, this result verifies the original work; if it did not match, then an error exists either in the original work or the check itself.)

Example: Check B2
Add to check subtraction, hence \$643.26 + \$556.74 = \$1,200.00. (Since the answer matches the original given quantity, this result verifies the original work.)

For each original calculation, the student can check his work by using the opposite operation to check the original work (except addition where one may simply rearrange the order of the addends).

Biblical Teaching Methods

"Games are to mathematics, what books are to reading, and experiments are to science."
(Joan Cotter, 1999)

Method	Biblical Documentation	Result
Agreeing/Disagreeing: Living in concord; settling by consent	"Again I say unto you, That if two of you shall *agree* on earth as touching any thing that they shall ask, it shall be done for them of my Father which is in heaven." (Matthew 18:19) "I hope all of you who are mature Christians will see eye-to-eye with me on these things, and if you *disagree* on some point, I believe that God will make it plain to you—if you fully obey the truth you have." (Philippians 3:15–16, Living Bible)	Cultivates the independent and free-thinking citizen able to sustain a Christian constitutional republic.
Analyzing: Resolving into elements, constituent parts, or first principles (rudiments)	"I am *resolved* what to do, that, when I am put out of the stewardship, they may receive me into their houses." (Luke 16:4) "A time to kill, and a time to heal; a time to *break down*, and a time to build up." (Ecclesiastes 3:3)	Develops the problem-solving component of mathematics.
Arranging: Putting in due order or form	"In the tabernacle of the congregation without the vail, which is before the testimony, Aaron and his sons shall *order* it from evening to morning before the LORD: it shall be a statute for ever unto their generations on the behalf of the children of Israel." (Exodus 27:21) "The pure candlestick, with the lamps thereof, even with the lamps to be set in *order*, and all the vessels thereof, and the oil for light." (Exodus 39:37)	Develops orderliness and systematic thinking resulting in orderly classification of facts relating to any subject.
Associating: Uniting in company or in interest; joining	"Teach me thy way, O LORD; I will walk in thy truth: *unite* my heart to fear thy name." (Psalm 86:11) "They shall ask the way to Zion with their faces thitherward, saying, Come, and let us *join* ourselves to the LORD in a perpetual covenant that shall not be forgotten." (Jeremiah 50:5) "Then the Spirit said unto Philip, Go near, and *join* thyself to this chariot." (Acts 8:29)	Develops the connecting of ideas and demonstrates the union with diversity (partnership).
Comparing: Examining the relations of things to each other; likening	"*Examine* me, O LORD, and prove me; try my reins and my heart." (Psalm 26:2) "For who in the heaven can be *compared* unto the LORD? who among the sons of the mighty can be *likened* unto the LORD?" (Psalm 89:6) "For wisdom is better than rubies; and all the things that may be desired are not to be *compared* to it." (Proverbs 8:11) "But whereunto shall I *liken* this generation? It is like unto children sitting in the markets, and calling unto their fellows." (Matthew 11:16)	Teaches one to see the relations of things with a view to discover their relative proportions, quantities, or qualities. Upholds God's Principle of Individuality and the Christian Principle of Representation. It teaches quality as well as quantity. "If we rightly estimate what we call good and evil, we shall find it lies much in comparison." *(Locke)*
Concentrating: Bringing to a point or to closer union	"Let us hear the *conclusion* of the whole matter: Fear God, and keep his commandments: for this is the whole duty of man." (Ecclesiastes 12:13)	Teaches focus, union, a collection brought to a *conclusion*.

(Note: Emphasis added by author.)

Method	Biblical Documentation	Result
Constructing: Building; framing; composing	"And Noah *builded* an altar unto the LORD; and took of every clean beast, and of every clean fowl, and offered burnt offerings on the altar." (Genesis 8:20) "And the LORD appeared unto Abram, and said, Unto thy seed will I give this land: and there *builded* he an altar unto the LORD, who appeared unto him." (Genesis 12:7)	Develops understanding based upon a worthy model, yet includes the idea of personal invention; reduces theory into practice, and equations into lines and geometrical demonstrations; helps children think in subbase 5 and base 10; aids in seeing quantities and prepares children for thinking mathematically, especially geometrically.
Contrasting: Placing in opposition of two or more like things with a view to discover the difference of figures or other things, and exhibit the advantage or excellence of one beyond that of the other	"And that ye may put *difference* between holy and unholy, and between unclean and clean." (Leviticus 10:10) "Even the righteousness of God which is by faith of Jesus Christ unto all and upon all them that believe: for there is no *difference*." (Romans 3:22) "For there is no *difference* between the Jew and the Greek: for the same Lord over all is rich unto all that call upon him." (Romans 10:12) "And of some have compassion, making a *difference*." (Jude v. 22)	Teaches one to identify excellence over mediocrity. "To contrast the goodness of God with our rebellion will tend to make us humble and thankful." (Daniel Atkinson Clark, "Independence Sermon," July 4, 1814, Hanover, NJ)
Converting: Turning or changing; undergoing a change	"And said, Verily I say unto you, Except ye be *converted*, and become as little children, ye shall not enter into the kingdom of heaven." (Matthew 18:3) "Repent ye therefore, and be *converted*, that your sins may be blotted out, when the times of refreshing shall come from the presence of the Lord." (Acts 3:19) "But we all, with open face beholding as in a glass the glory of the Lord, are *changed* into the same image from glory to glory, even as by the Spirit of the Lord." (2 Corinthians 3:18)	Teaches one to appropriate or apply to one's own use; teaches one to make that which is learned useful—the reduction of equations by multiplication, or the manner of altering an equation when the quantity sought or any element of the equation is a fraction.
Distributing: Dividing among a number; dealing out	"Now when Jesus heard these things, he said unto him, Yet lackest thou one thing: sell all that thou hast, and *distribute* unto the poor, and thou shalt have treasure in heaven: and come, follow me." (Luke 18:22) "And Jesus took the loaves; and when he had given thanks, he *distributed* to the disciples, and the disciples to them that were set down; and likewise of the fishes as much as they would." (John 6:11) "*Distributing* to the necessity of saints; given to hospitality." (Romans 12:13)	Demonstrates the distributive principle.
Drawing: Representing the appearance or figures of objects on a plain surface by means of lines and shades, as with a pencil, crayon, pen, compass, delineation	"Thus he shewed me: and, behold, the LORD stood upon a wall made by a *plumbline*. Then said the Lord, Behold, I will set a *plumbline* in the midst of my people Israel." (Amos 7:7–8)	Develops ownership of one's understanding of a subject by giving this understanding personal external expression; develops the habit of making a record and keeping it plain; develops internal vision.
Engineering: Forming plans by those skilled in mathematics	"And I arose in the night, I and some few men with me; neither told I any man what my God had put in my heart to do at Jerusalem: . . . "And I went out by night . . . and viewed the walls of Jerusalem, which were broken down." (Nehemiah 2:12–13)	Teaches and develops the art of problem solving while developing the art of self-government in imitation of God, who providentially superintends over His creation.

Method	Biblical Documentation	Result
Estimating: Valuing; forming an opinion or judgment of the value, extent, quantity, or degree of worth of any object; calculating; computing	"And when a man shall sanctify his house to be holy unto the LORD, then the priest shall *estimate* it, whether it be good or bad: as the priest shall *estimate* it, so shall it stand." (Leviticus 27:14)	Exercises one's ability to form an opinion without actually measuring or weighing; teaches the art of computation.
Exchanging: Giving and receiving one commodity for another; giving and receiving mutually	"For what is a man profited, if he shall gain the whole world, and lose his own soul? or what shall a man give in *exchange* for his soul?" (Matthew 16:26)	Teaches like value of different commodities. Teaches Biblical reciprocity; demonstrates the commutative principle of mathematics.
Extending: Stretching, enlarging; valuing; spreading	"And hath *extended* mercy unto me before the king, and his counsellors, and before all the king's mighty princes. And I was strengthened as the hand of the LORD my God was upon me, and I gathered together out of Israel chief men to go up with me." (Ezra 7:28)	Teaches one to draw upon what is known and apply it or demonstrate it in unfamiliar situations. (Ex: Taking mere data from one word problem and then using it to teach graphing.)
Graphing: Writing or delineating accurately	"It seemed good to me also, having had perfect understanding of all things from the very first, to *write* unto thee in order, most excellent Theophilus." (Luke 1:3)	Teaches the art of communicating mathematical ideas visually (in pictures) and accurately, so the idea is more easily understood.
Inspecting: Looking on or into; viewing with care; examining to ascertain the quality or condition	"Who, when they had *examined* me, would have let me go, because there was no cause of death in me." (Acts 28:18)	Teaches superintendence, an attribute of God; teaches one to look for quality; teaches the Christian character trait of brotherly love and carefulness; teaches duty of oversight/guardianship.
Journaling: Keeping a daily account of events, discoveries, and improvements in arts and sciences	"And this is the *record* of John, when the Jews sent priests and Levites from Jerusalem to ask him, Who art thou?" (John 1:19)	Develops the habit of keeping a notebook that is essential to the work of mathematics and science; teaches the habit of recording newly learned or discovered principles, rules, and ideas.
Listening: Hearkening; attending closely with a view to obey or yield to advice	"*Hearken*; Behold, there went out a sower to sow." (Mark 4:3) "*Hearken*, my beloved brethren, Hath not God chosen the poor of this world rich in faith, and heirs of the kingdom which he hath promised to them that love him?" (James 2:5)	Develops listening skills that aid in the development of faith that comes by hearing. Gives one opportunity to obey what is heard.
Matching: Equaling; setting in opposition; uniting	"Teach me thy way, O LORD; I will walk in thy truth: *unite* my heart to fear thy name." (Psalm 86:11)	Teaches equality (=). Teaches that which is suitable or fit to be joined, a life skill used to show which items belong together (fruit with a seed, shoes with socks); demonstrates the associative principle of mathematics.
Measuring: The whole extent or dimensions of a thing, including length, breadth, and thickness	"For we dare not make ourselves of the number, or compare ourselves with some that commend themselves: but they *measuring* themselves by themselves, and comparing themselves among themselves, are not wise." (2 Corinthians 10:12)	Teaches the art of computation; teaches limits, proportion, quantity, and dimensions (length, width, height, capacity, amount).

Method	Biblical Documentation	Result
Notating: Recording anything by marks, figures, or characters; particularly in arithmetic and algebra, expressing numbers and quantities by figures, signs or characters appropriate for the purpose	"And the LORD said unto him, Therefore whosoever slayeth Cain, vengeance shall be taken on him sevenfold. And the LORD set a *mark* upon Cain, lest any finding him should kill him." (Genesis 4:15) "And he asked for a writing table, and *wrote*, saying, His name is John. And they marvelled all." (Luke 1:63)	Employs, demonstrates, and instructs the learner in the Christian Principles of Individuality, Representation, Conscience, and Character; demonstrates math as a language by using universal symbols to express mathematical ideas.
Ordinal Counting: Noting order	"Many of them also which used curious arts brought their books together, and burned them before all men: and they *counted* the price of them, and found it fifty thousand pieces of silver." (Acts 19:19)	Teaches orderliness and demonstrates sequential methodical thinking; helps sustain representation by naming quantity.
Partitioning: Dividing, separating	"So Solomon overlaid the house within with pure gold: and he made a *partition* by the chains of gold before the oracle; and he overlaid it with gold." (1 Kings 6:21) "For he is our peace, who hath made both one, and hath broken down the middle wall of *partition* between us." (Ephesians 2:14)	Demonstrates, teaches, and upholds the distinctiveness of things according to God's Principle of Individuality; enables one to see the parts of the whole; develops the skill of breaking things down into smaller parts—analysis; demonstrates the distributive principle of mathematics.
Problem Solving: Resolving any question requiring some operation or experiment	"And Jesus increased in *wisdom* and stature, and in favour with God and man." (Luke 2:52) "Can two walk together, except they be *agreed*?" (Amos 3:3)	Teaches one to apply knowledge in known situations to unfamiliar ones; enables one to convert knowledge to wisdom.
Proving: Ascertaining some unknown quality or truth by an experiment, or by a test or standard	"But Saul increased the more in strength, and confounded the Jews which dwelt at Damascus, *proving* that this is very Christ." (Acts 9:22) "*Proving* what is acceptable unto the Lord." (Ephesians 5:10)	Teaches by demonstration the judicial function of our American Christian form of government; teaches truth as absolute by argument, induction, or reasoning; teaches the learner to verify knowledge; teaches one to show, evince, or ascertain the correctness of any operation or result based upon the principles governing the subject.
Recognizing Patterns: Acknowledging as known that which is to be imitated (an exemplar), either in things or in actions	"For we write none other things unto you, than what ye read or *acknowledge*; and I trust ye shall *acknowledge* even to the end." (2 Corinthians 1:13) "According to all that I *shew* thee, after the pattern of the tabernacle, and the pattern of all the instruments thereof, even so shall ye make it." (Exodus 25:9)	Teaches the ability to imitate or copy that which is exemplary—as Christ is the most perfect pattern of rectitude, patience, and submission ever exhibited on earth—to enhance problem-solving skills, sound reasoning, and develop wholesome scholarship; aids in developing the ability to visualize quantities.
Reflecting: Considering attentively; contemplating	"Now therefore, I pray thee, if I have found grace in thy sight, shew me now thy way, that I may know thee, that I may find grace in thy sight: and *consider* that this nation is thy people." (Exodus 33:13) "Know therefore this day, and *consider* it in thine heart, that the LORD he is God in heaven above, and upon the earth beneath: there is none else." (Deuteronomy 4:39) "Hearken unto this, O Job: stand still, and *consider* the wondrous works of God." (Job 37:14) "And why take ye thought for raiment? *Consider* the lilies of the field, how they grow; they toil not, neither do they spin." (Matthew 6:28)	Teaches one to remember and reconsider past thoughts, opinions or decisions of the mind, and past events that may result in joy; causes growth and improvement.

Method	Biblical Documentation	Result
Representing: Showing; exhibiting; describing	"And thou shalt teach them ordinances and laws, and shalt *shew* them the way wherein they must walk." (Exodus 18:20)	Teaches the Christian Principle of Representation essential to the language and understanding of mathematics.
Researching: Seeking truth diligently	"These were more noble than those in Thessalonica, in that they received the word with all readiness of mind, and *searched* the scriptures daily, whether those things were so." (Acts 17:11) "*Search* the scriptures." (John 5:39)	Develops an attribute of the Holy Spirit and God in the learner; teaches inquiry, carefulness, and diligence in seeking facts or principles; teaches labor (hard work).
Sketching: Drawing the outline	"When He established the heavens, I was there, When He *inscribed* a circle on the face of the deep." (Proverbs 8:27, NASB)	Teaches one to make a rough draft, or plan, or design before acting; teaches one to think wholistically and to consider consequences first, before taking action (problem solving).
Sorting: Separating things having like qualities from other things, and placing them in distinct classes or divisions in an orderly fashion; reducing to order from a state of confusion	"And of every living thing of all flesh, two of every *sort* shalt thou bring into the ark, to keep them alive with thee; they shall be male and female." (Genesis 6:19) Every man's work shall be made manifest: for the day shall declare it, because it shall be revealed by fire; and the fire shall try every man's work of what *sort* it is." (1 Corinthians 3:13)	Teaches God's Principle of Individuality according to likenesses or differences (color, size, etc.); teaches one to see distinctive qualities of objects so essential in science and mathematics.
Subitizing: Recognizing quantities quickly without the aid of counting	"And she gave the king 120 talents of gold, *large quantities* of spices, and precious stones." (1 Kings 10:10, NIV) "And they shall hang upon him all the glory of his father's house, the offspring and the issue, all vessels of *small quantity*, from the vessels of cups, even to all the vessels of flagons." (Isaiah 22:24)	Teaches confidence and the art of computation; lends speed to accuracy of computation.
Summarizing: Giving a brief or concise account of what is fully known	"But I say unto you, That every idle word that men shall speak, they shall *give account* thereof in the day of judgment." (Matthew 12:36) "So then every one of us shall *give account* of himself to God." (Romans 14:12)	Causes one to reduce into a few words a compendious process; develops succinct, concise, accurate, and precise communication using the language of mathematics.
Synthesizing: Putting two or more things together; the opposite of analyzing	"Wherefore they are no more twain, but one flesh. What therefore God hath *joined together*, let not man put asunder." (Matthew 19:6)	Teaches diligent use of principled reasoning till one arrives at a conclusion; demonstrates unity with union and diversity.
Tallying: Agreeing; corresponding; fitting to each other	"During the reign of Darius the Persian, a *record* was also kept of the Levites and priests." (Nehemiah 12:22, NKJV) The LORD will *record*, When He registers the peoples." (Psalm 87:6, NKJV)	Teaches one to keep records as a precursor to the art and science of bookkeeping and accounting. (Games often keep score or tally, i.e., runs, hits, and errors.) Before the use of writing, this or something like it was the only method of keeping accounts, and tallies are received as evidence in courts of justice.

Method	Biblical Documentation	Result
Translating: Conveying or rendering into another language; expressing the sense of one language in the words or symbols of another; interpreting in another language	"Inasmuch as an excellent spirit, knowledge, understanding, *interpreting* dreams, solving riddles, and explaining enigmas were found in this Daniel." (Daniel 5:12, NKJV) "but he hanged the chief baker, just as Joseph had *interpreted* to them." (Genesis 40:22, NASB) "Behold, a virgin shall be with child, and bear a Son, and they shall call His name Immanuel," which is *translated*, "God with us." (Matthew 1:23, NKJV)	Demonstrates that quantities can be represented in various ways (fingers, tally sticks, abacus, etc.) in the diverse language of mathematics; teaches one to operate with many different written symbols and other representations (i.e., abacus, spoken word, written numeral, tally sticks, fingers), and to express oneself with equivalent words.
Visualizing: Imagining based upon earlier proven fact and principle	"For whom he did foreknow, he also did predestinate to be conformed to the *image* of his Son, that he might be the firstborn among many brethren." (Romans 8:29)	Enables the student to subitize (see quantity); each prepares the student to think mathematically.

Michelangelo Buonarroti, *Prophet Daniel*, 1512, Sistine Chapel, Vatican City

Appendix

This most beautiful system of sun, planets, and comets could only proceed from the counsel and dominion of an intelligent and powerful Being. . . . This Being governs all things, not as the Soul of the world, but as Lord over all.

(Sir Isaac Newton, *Principia*, 1687)

Glossary of Terms

(Definitions taken primarily from Webster's 1828 *Dictionary.*)

abstract, *a.* Separate; distinct from something else. An *abstract* idea, in metaphysics, is an idea separated from a complex object, or from other ideas which naturally accompany it, as the solidity of marble contemplated apart from its color or figure. *Abstract* numbers are numbers used without application to things, as, 6, 8, 10: but when applied to any thing, as 6 feet, 10 men, they become concrete. *Abstract* or pure mathematics, is that which treats of magnitude or quantity, without restriction to any species of particular magnitude, as arithmetic and geometry; opposed to which is mixed mathematics, which treats of simple properties, and the relations of quantity, as applied to sensible objects, as hydrostatics, navigation, optics, &c.

addition, *n.* [L. *additio,* from *addo.*] 1. The act of adding, opposed to subtraction, or diminution; as, a sum is increased by *addition.* 2. Any thing added, whether material or immaterial. 3. In *arithmetic,* the uniting of two or more numbers in one sum; also the rule or branch of arithmetic which treats of adding numbers. *Simple* addition is the joining of sums of the same denominations, as pounds to pounds, dollars to dollars. *Compound* addition is the joining of sums of different denominations, as dollars and cents.

adjacent, *a.* Lying near, close, or contiguous; bordering upon; as, a field *adjacent* to the highway.

algebra, *n.* [Ar. the reduction of parts to a whole, or fractions to whole numbers, from the verb, which signifies to consolidate; Heb. to be strong.] The science of quantity in general, or universal arithmetic. Algebra is a general method of computation, in which signs and symbols, which are commonly the letters of the alphabet, are made to represent numbers and quantities. It takes a known quantity sought, as if granted; and, by means of one or more quantities given, proceeds till the quantity supposed is discovered, by some other known quantity to which it is equal.

altitude, *n.* Space extended upward; height; the elevation of an object above its foundation; as, the *altitude* of a mountain, or column; or the elevation of an object or place above the surface on which we stand, or above the earth; as, the *altitude* of a cloud or a meteor; or the elevation of one object above another; as, of a bird above the top of a tree.

analysis, *n.* In *mathematics,* analysis is the resolving of problems by algebraic equations. The analysis of finite quantities is otherwise called algebra, or specious arithmetic. The analysis of infinites is the method of fluxions, or the differential calculus.

angle, *n.* In *popular language,* the point where two lines meet, or the meeting of two lines in a point; a corner.

In *geometry,* the space comprised between two straight lines that meet in a point, or between two straight converging lines which, if extended, would meet; or the quantity by which two straight lines, departing from a point, diverge from each other. The point of meeting is the vertex of the angle, and the lines, containing the angle, are its sides or legs.

antecedent, *n.* In *mathematics,* the first of two terms of a ratio, or that which is compared with the other.

arc, *n.* In *geometry,* any part of the circumference of a circle, or curved line, lying from one point to another; a segment, or part of a circle, not more than a semicircle.

area, *n.* 1. Any plain surface, as the floor of a room, of a church or other building, or of the ground. 2. In *geometry,* the superficial contents of any figure; the surface included within any given lines; as the *area* of a square or a triangle.

arithmetic, *n.* [Gr. to number, the art of numbering, from number; rhythm, order, agreement.] The science of numbers, or the art of computation. The various operations of arithmetic are performed by addition, subtraction, multiplication and division.

average, *v.t.* To find the mean of unequal sums or quantities; to reduce to a medium; to divide among a number, according to a given proportion; as to *average* a loss.

axiom, *n.* 1. A self-evident truth, or a proposition whose truth is so evident at first sight, that no process of reasoning or demonstration can make it plainer; as, "the whole is greater than a part." 2. An established principle in some art or science; a principle received without new proof; as, "things which are equal to the same thing, are equal to one another."

axis, *n.* 1. The straight line, real or imaginary, passing through a body, on which it revolves, or may revolve; as the *axis* of the earth. 2. In geometry, a straight line in a plain figure, about which it revolves to produce a solid. 3. In conic sections, a right line dividing the section into two equal parts, and cutting all its ordinates at right angles.

base, *n.* 1. The bottom of any thing, considered as its support or the part of a thing on which it stands or rests; as the *base* of a column, the pedestal of a statue, the foundation of a house, &c. 2. In *geometry,* the lowest side of the perimeter of a figure. Any side of a triangle may be called its *base,* but this term most properly belongs to the side which is parallel to the horizon. In rectangled triangles, the base, properly, is the side opposite to the right angle. The *base* of a solid figure is that on which it stands. The *base* of a conic section is a right line in the hyperbola and parabola, arising from the common intersection of the secant plane and the base of the cone.

billion, *n.* [*bis* and *million.*] 1. A thousand million or 10^9; 2. (Brit.) A million millions, or 10^{12}. (Webster's 1984 *Dictionary*)

binomial, *a.* [L. *bis,* twice, and *nomen,* name.] In *algebra,* a root consisting of two members connected by the sign plus or minus; as $a + b$, or $7 - 3$.

bisect, *v.t.* To cut or divide into two parts. In *geometry,* one line *bisects* another when it crosses it, leaving an equal part of the line on each side of the point where it is crossed.

bond, *n.* 1. Any thing that binds, as a cord, a chain, a rope; a band. 2. An obligation imposing a moral duty, as by a vow, or promise, by law or other means. 3. In *law* (*Blackstone*), an obligation or deed by which a person binds himself, his heirs, executors, and administrators, to pay a certain sum, on or before a future day appointed. This is a single bond. But usually a condition is added, that if the obligor shall do a certain act, or pay a certain sum of money, on or before a time specified, the obligation shall be void; otherwise it shall remain in full force. If the condition is not performed, the bond becomes forfeited, and the obligor and his heirs are liable to the payment of the whole sum.

brokerage, *n.* The fee, reward or commission given or charged for transacting business as a broker.

cancel, *v.t.* To cross the lines of a writing, and deface them; to blot out or obliterate.

cancelation, *n.* The act of defacing by cross lines; a canceling.

chord, *n.* In *geometry,* a right line drawn or supposed to extend from one end of an arch of a circle to the other. Hence, the chord of an arch is a right line joining the extremities of that arch.

circle, *n.* In *geometry,* a plane figure comprehended by a single curve line, called its circumference, every part of which is equally distant from a point called the center. Of course all lines drawn from the center to the circumference or periphery, are equal to each other.

circumference, *n.* The line that bounds a circle; the exterior line of a circular body; the whole exterior surface of a round body; a periphery.

coefficient, *n.* In *algebra,* a number or known quantity put before letters, or quantities, known or unknown, and into which it is supposed to be multiplied; as in $3x$ and ax, 3 and a are the coefficients of x.

commission, *n.* The allowance made to a factor or commission-merchant for transacting business, which is a certain rate per cent of the value of the goods bought or sold.

complement, *n.* 1. In *geometry,* what remains of the quadrant of a circle, or of ninety degrees, after any arch has been taken from it. Thus if the arch taken is thirty degrees, its complement is sixty. 2. *Arithmetical complement* of a logarithm, is what the logarithm wants of 10,000,000.

concrete, *a.* A *concrete* number expresses or denotes a particular subject, as *three* men; but when we use a number without reference to a subject, as *three,* or *five,* we use the term in the abstract. *Bailey.*

conic sections, conics, *n.* That part of geometry which treats of the cone and the curves which arise from its sections. A curve line formed by the intersection of a cone and plane. The conic sections are the parabola, hyperbola, and ellipsis.

consequent, *n.* In arithmetic, the name given to the second term in a ratio. The result obtained when dividing the antecedent by the ratio.

cosine, *n.* In *geometry,* the sine of an arc which is the complement of another to ninety degrees.

curve, *n.* A bending in a regular form, or without angles; that which is bent; a flexure; part of a circle. In *geometry,* a line which may be cut by a right line in more points than one.

cylinder, *n.* In *geometry,* a solid body supposed to be generated by the rotation of a parallelogram round one of its sides; or a long circular body of uniform diameter, and its extremities forming equal parallel circles.

decimal, *a.* Numbered by ten. 2. Increasing or diminishing by ten; as *decimal* numbers; *decimal* arithmetic; *decimal* fractions. 3. Tenth; as a *decimal* part.

degree, *n*. In *geometry*, a division of a circle, including a three hundred and sixtieth part of its circumference. Hence a *degree of latitude* is the 360th part of the earth's surface north or south of the equator, and a *degree of longitude*, the same part of the surface east or west of any given meridian.

demonstrable, *a*. That may be demonstrated; that may be proved beyond doubt or contradiction; capable of being shown by certain evidence, or by evidence that admits of no doubt; as, the principles of geometry are *demonstrable*.

denominator, *n*. He that gives a name. 2. In arithmetic, that number placed below the line in common fractions, which shows into how many parts the integer is divided. Thus in $\frac{3}{5}$, 5 is the *denominator*, showing that the integer is divided into five parts; and the numerator 3 shows how many parts are taken, that is, *three fifths*.

diagonal, *a*. In *geometry*, extending from one angle to another of a quadrilateral figure, and dividing it into two equal parts.

diagonal, *n*. A right line drawn from angle to angle of a quadrilateral figure, as a square or parallelogram, and dividing it into two equal parts. It is sometimes called the *diameter*, and sometimes the *diametral*.

diameter, *n*. A right line passing through the center of a circle or other curvilinear figure, terminated by the circumference, and dividing the figure into two equal parts.

difference, *n*. In *mathematics*, the remainder of a sum or quantity, after a lesser sum or quantity is subtracted.

discount, *n*. A sum deducted for prompt or advanced payment; an allowance or deduction from a sum due, or from a credit; a certain rate per cent deducted from the credit price of goods sold, on account of prompt payment; or any deduction from the customary price, or from a sum due or to be due at a future time. Thus the merchant who gives a credit of three months will deduct a certain rate per cent for payment in hand, and the holder of a note or bill of exchange will deduct a certain rate per cent of the amount of the note or bill for advanced payment, which deduction is called a *discount*. 2. Among *bankers*, the deduction of a sum for advanced payment; particularly, the deduction of the interest on a sum lent, at the time of lending. The discounts at banking institutions are usually the amount of legal interest paid by the borrower, and deducted from the sum borrowed, at the commencement of the credit. 3. The sum deducted or refunded; as, the *discount* was five per cent.

dividend, *n*. A part or share; particularly, the share of the interest or profit of stock in trade or other employment, which belongs to each proprietor according to his proportion of the stock or capital. 2. In *arithmetic*, the number to be divided into equal parts.

division, *n*. In *arithmetic*, the dividing of a number or quantity into any parts assigned; or the rule by which is found how many times one number is contained in another.

divisor, *n*. In *arithmetic*, the number by which the dividend is divided.

equation, *n*. In *algebra*, a proposition asserting the equality of two quantities, and expressed by the sign = between them; or an expression of the same quantity in two dissimilar terms, but of equal value, as 3s = 36d, or $x = b + m - r$. In the latter case, x is equal to b added to m, with r subtracted, and the quantities on the right hand of the sign of equation are said to be the value of x on the left hand.

equilateral, *n*. A side exactly corresponding to others.

evolution, *n*. [the act of unfolding or unrolling.] In [arithmetic and] *algebra*, evolution is the extraction of roots from powers; the reverse of involution.

excellence, *n*. [Fr. from L. *excellentia*.] The state of possessing good qualities in an unusual or eminent degree; the state of excelling in any thing. 2. Any valuable quality; any thing highly laudable, meritorious or virtuous, in persons, or valuable and esteemed, in things.

exchange, *n*. In *commerce*, the act of giving one thing or commodity for another; barter; traffic by permutation, in which the thing received is supposed to be equivalent to the thing given.

exponent, *n*. In *algebra*, the number or figure which, placed above a root at the right hand, denotes how often that root is repeated, or how many multiplications are necessary to produce the power. Thus, a^2 denotes the second power of the root a, or aa: a^4 denotes the fourth power. The figure is the exponent or index of the power.

factor, *n*. In *arithmetic*, the multiplier and multiplicand, from the multiplication of which proceeds the product.

figure, *n*. In *arithmetic*, a character denoting a number; as 2. 7. 9.

formula, *n*. In *mathematics*, a general expression for resolving certain cases or problems.

fraction, *n*. In *arithmetic* and *algebra*, a broken part of an integral or integer; any division of a whole number or unit, as $\frac{2}{5}$, two fifths, $\frac{1}{4}$, one fourth, which are called *common fractions*.

In these, the figure above the line is called the *numerator,* and the figure below the line the *denominator*. In *decimal fractions,* the denominator is a unit, or 1, with as many ciphers annexed, as the numerator has places. They are commonly expressed by writing the numerator only, with a point before it by which it is separated from the whole number; thus .5, which denotes five tenths, $\frac{5}{10}$, or half the whole number; .25, that is $\frac{25}{100}$, or a fourth part of the whole number.

function, *n.* In *mathematics*, the *function* of a variable quantity, is any algebraic expression into which that quantity enters, mixed with other quantities that have invariable values.

geometry, *n.* [Gr. the earth, and measure.] Originally and properly, the art of measuring the earth, or any distances or dimensions on it. But geometry now denotes the science of magnitude in general, comprehending the doctrine and relations of whatever is susceptible of augmentation and diminution; as the mensuration of lines, surfaces, solids, velocity, weight, &c. with their various relations.

hexagon, *n.* In *geometry*, a figure of six sides and six angles. If the sides and angles are equal, it is a *regular hexagon*. The cells of honeycomb are hexagons, and it is remarkable that bees instinctively form their cells of this figure which fills any given space without any interstice or loss of room.

hypotenuse, *n.* In *geometry*, the subtense or longest side of a right-angled triangle, or the line that subtends the right angle.

hypothesis, *n.* 1. A supposition; a proposition or principle which is supposed or taken for granted, in order to draw a conclusion or inference for proof of the point in question; something not proved, but assumed for the purpose of argument. 2. A system or theory imagined or assumed to account for what is not understood.

inequality, *n.* Difference or want of equality in degree, quantity, length, or quality of any kind; the state of not having equal measure, degree, dimensions or amount; as an *inequality* in size or stature; an *inequality* of numbers or of power; *inequality* of distances or of motions.

insurance, *n.* The act of insuring or assuring against loss or damage; or a contract by which one engages for a stipulated consideration or premium per cent, to make up a loss which another may sustain. *Insurance* is usually made on goods or property exposed to uncommon hazard, or on lives. 2. The premium paid for insuring property or life. *Insurance company,* a company or corporation whose business is to insure against loss or damage.

interest, *n.* Premium paid for the use of money; the profit per cent derived from money lent, or property used by another person, or from debts remaining unpaid. A higher rate of *interest* than that which the law allows, is called *usury*. *Simple interest* is that which arises from the principal sum only. *Compound interest* is that which arises from the principal with the interest added; interest on interest.

involution, *n.* In *algebra*, the raising of a quantity from its root to any power assigned. Thus 2 x 2 x 2 = 8. Here 8, the third power of 2, is found by *involution*, or multiplying the number into itself, and the product by the same number.

isosceles, *a.* Having two legs only that are equal.

latitude, *n.* Breadth; width; extent from side to side.

length, *n.* The extent of any thing material from end to end; the longest line which can be drawn through a body, parallel to its sides; as the *length* of a church or of a ship; the *length* of a rope or line. 2. Extent; extension. 3. Space of time; duration, indefinitely; as a great *length* of time.

line, *n.* In *geometry*, a quantity extended in length, without breadth or thickness; or a limit terminating a surface.

liter, *n.* A French measure of capacity, being a cubic decimeter, containing, according to Lunier, about a pint and a half old French measure. The liter is equal to 60.0280 cubic inches.

logarithm, *n.* [Fr. *Logarithme;* Gr. ratio, and number.] Logarithms are the exponents of a series of powers and roots. The logarithm of a number is that exponent of some other number, which renders the power of the latter, denoted by the exponent, equal to the former. When the logarithms form a series in arithmetical progression, the corresponding natural numbers form a series in geometrical progression. Thus,

Logarithms	0	1	2	3	4	5
Natural numbers	1	10	100	1000	10000	100000

The addition and subtraction of logarithms answer to the multiplication and division of their natural numbers. In like manner, involution is performed by multiplying the logarithm of any number by the number denoting the required power; and evolution, by dividing the logarithm by the number denoting the required root. Logarithms are the invention of Baron Napier, lord of Marchiston in Scotland; but the kind now in use, were invented by Henry Briggs, professor of geometry in Gresham college, at Oxford. They are extremely useful in abridging the labor of trigonometrical calculations.

longitude, *n*. The distance of any place on the globe from another place, eastward or westward; or the distance of any place from a given meridian. Boston, in Massachusetts, is situated in the 71st degree of *longitude* west from Greenwich. To be able to ascertain precisely the *longitude* of a ship at sea, is a great desideratum in navigation.

loss, *n*. Privation; as the *loss* of property; *loss* of money by gaming; *loss* of health or reputation. Every loss is not a detriment. We cannot regret the *loss* of bad company or of evil habits. 2. Waste; useless application; as a *loss* of time or labor.

magnitude, *n*. [L. *magnitudo*.] Extent of dimensions or parts; bulk; size; applied to things that have length, breadth or thickness.

mathematics, *n*. 1. The language of God expressed in creation, the patterns of which laid the structure of the universe and describe the laws of His handiwork. (Editor)
2. Mathematics describes the set of perpetual laws with which God made manifest and upholds the physical universe. It is the expression of His orderly nature that describes the quantitative relationships governing the individual members of creation, from the micro- to the macro-cosmos (Hebrews 1:3; Colossians 1:17) (Editor)
3. An entity which perhaps always exists in the mind of God, and which is for man the universal expression of His creative and sustaining word of power. (Larry Zimmerman)

mathematics, *n*. [L. *mathematica*, from Gr. to learn] The science of quantity; the science which treats of magnitude and number, or of whatever can be measured or numbered. This science is divided into *pure* or *speculative*, which considers quantity abstractly, without relation to matter; and *mixed*, which treats of magnitude as subsisting in material bodies, and is consequently interwoven with physical considerations. It is the peculiar excellence of *mathematics*, that its principles are demonstrable. Arithmetic, geometry, algebra, trigonometry, and conic sections, are branches of *mathematics*.

measure, *n*. [Fr. *mesure;* G. *mass*, measure; L. *mensura* from *mensus*, to measure; Eng. to *mete*. The sense is to come to, to fall, to happen, and this sense is connected with that of stretching, extending.] The whole extent or dimensions of a thing, including length, breadth and thickness. "The *measure* thereof is longer than the earth and broader than the sea." Job 11. 2. That by which extent or dimension is ascertained, either length, breadth, thickness, capacity, or amount; as, a rod or pole is a measure of five yards and a half; an inch, a foot, a yard, are *measures* of length; a gallon is a *measure* of capacity. Weights and *measures* should be uniform. Silver and gold are the common *measure* of value. 3. In geometry, any quantity assumed as one or unity, to which the ratio of other homogeneous or similar quantities is expressed.

measure, *v.t.* To compute or ascertain extent, quantity, dimensions, or capacity by a certain rule; as, to *measure* land; to *measure* distance; to *measure* the altitude of a mountain; to *measure* the capacity of a ship or of a cask.

meter, *n*. A French measure of length. The standard of linear measure, being the ten millionth part of the distance from the equator to the North Pole, as ascertained by actual measurement of an arc of the meridian.

millimeter, *n*. A French lineal measure containing the thousandth part of a meter; equal to .03937 decimals of an inch.

million, *n*. The number of ten hundred thousand, or a thousand thousand.

minuend, *n*. In *arithmetic*, the number from which another number is to be subtracted.

monomial, *n*. In *algebra*, a quantity expressed by one name or letter.

multiplicand, *n*. In *arithmetic*, the number to be multiplied by another, which is called the multiplier.

multiplication, *n*. The act of multiplying or of increasing number; as the *multiplication* of the human species by natural generation. 2. In *arithmetic*, a rule or operation by which any given number may be increased according to any number of times proposed. Thus 10 multiplied by 5 is increased to 50.

multiplier, *n*. The number in arithmetic by which another is multiplied.

net, *a*. Being beyond all charges or outlay; as *net* profits.

notation, *n*. The act or practice of recording any thing by marks, figures, or characters; particularly in arithmetic and algebra, the expressing of numbers and quantities by figures, signs or characters appropriate for the purpose.

number, *n*. The designation of a unit in reference to other units, or in reckoning, counting, enumerating; as, one is the first *number;* a simple *number*. 2. In *mathematics*, number is variously distinguished. *Cardinal numbers* are those which express the amount of units; as 1.2.3.4.5.6.7.8.9.10. *Ordinal numbers* are those which express order; as first, second, third, fourth, &c. *Determinate number*, is that referred to a given unit, as a ternary or three; an *indeterminate number* is referred to unity in general, and called quantity. *Homogeneal*

numbers, are those referred to the same units; those referred to different units are termed *heterogeneal. Whole numbers* are called *integers*.

A *rational number* is one commensurable with unity. A number incommensurable with unity, is termed *irrational* or *surd*. A *prime* or *primitive number,* is divisible only by unity; as three, five, seven, &c. A *perfect number* is that whose aliquot parts added together, make the whole number, as 28, whose aliquot parts, 14.7.4.2.1., make the number 28. An *imperfect number* is that whose aliquot parts added together, make more or less than the number. This is abundant or defective; abundant, is 12, whose aliquot parts, 6.4.3.2.1., make 16; or defective, as 16, whose aliquot parts, 8.4.2.1. make 15 only. A *square number,* is the product of a number multiplied by itself; as, 16 is the square number of 4. A *cubic number,* is the product of a square number by its root; as, 27 is the product of the square number 9 by its root 3.

numeral, *a*. Pertaining to number; consisting of number. 2. Expressing number; representing number; standing as a substitute for figures; as *numeral* letters; as X for 10; L for fifty; C for 100, D for 500; M for 1000. 3. Expressing numbers; as *numeral* characters. The figures we now use to express numbers are 1. 2. 3. 4. 5. 6. 7. 8. 9. 0.

numeration, *n*. The act or art of numbering. 2. In *arithmetic,* notation; the art of expressing in characters any number proposed in words, or of expressing in words any number proposed in characters; the act or art of writing or reading numbers. Thus we write 1000, for thousand, and 50, we read fifty.

numerator, *n*. One that numbers. 2. In *arithmetic,* the number in common fractions which shows how many parts of a unit are taken. Thus when a unit is divided into 9 parts, and we take 5, we express it thus, $\frac{5}{9}$, that is, five ninths; 5 being the *numerator,* and 9 the *denominator*.

oblique, *a*. Deviating from a right line; not direct; not perpendicular; not parallel; aslant. It has a direction *oblique* to that of the former motion. An *oblique* angle is either acute or obtuse; any angle except a right one. An *oblique* line is one that, falling on another, makes oblique angles with it. *Oblique* planes, in dialing, are those which decline from the zenith, or incline towards the horizon. *Oblique* sailing, is when a ship sails upon some rhomb between the four cardinal points, making an oblique angle with the meridian.

obtuse, *a*. Blunt; not pointed or acute. Applied to angles, it denotes one that is larger than a right angle, or more than ninety degrees.

octagon, *n*. In *geometry,* a figure of eight sides and eight angles. When the sides and angles are equal, it is a regular octagon which may be inscribed in a circle.

order, *n*. The place a figure occupies in a number.

parallelogram, *n*. In *geometry,* a right lined quadrilateral figure, whose opposite sides are parallel and equal.

peculiar, *a*. [L. *peculiaris,* from *peculium,* one's own property, from *pecus,* cattle.] Appropriate; belonging to a person and to him only. Almost every writer has a *peculiar* style. Most men have manners *peculiar* to themselves. 2. Singular; particular. The man has something *peculiar* in his deportment. 3. Particular; special.

pentagon, *n*. In *geometry,* a figure of five sides and five angles.

perimeter, *n*. In *geometry,* the bounds and limits of a body or figure. The *perimeters* of surfaces or figures are lines; those of bodies are surfaces. In circular figures, instead of *perimeter,* we use *circumference* or *periphery*.

perpendicular, *a*. In *geometry,* falling directly on another line at right angles. The line A is *perpendicular* to the line B.

perpendicular, *n*. In *geometry,* a line falling at right angles on another line, or making equal angles with it on each side.

plane, *n*. In *geometry,* an even or level surface.

polygon, *n*. In *geometry,* a figure of many angles and sides, and whose perimeter consists at least of more than four sides.

polyhedron, *n*. In *geometry,* a body or solid contained under many sides or planes.

polynomial, *a*. Containing many names or terms.

power, *n*. In *arithmetic* and *algebra,* the product arising from the multiplication of a number or quantity into itself; as, a cube is the third *power;* the biquadrate is the fourth *power*.

premium, *n*. The recompense to underwriters for insurance, or for undertaking to indemnify for losses of any kind. 2. It is sometimes synonymous with interest, but generally in obtaining loans, it is a sum per cent distinct from the interest. The bank lends money to government at a *premium* of 2 per cent.

principal, *n*. In *commerce,* a capital sum lent on interest, due as a debt or used as a fund; so called in distinction from *interest* or *profits*.

principle, *n*. [L. *principium,* beginning.] In a *general sense,* the cause, source or origin of any thing; that from which a

thing proceeds; as the *principle* of motion; the *principles* of action. 2. Element; constituent part; primordial substance. 3. Being that produces any thing; operative cause. 4. In *science*, a truth admitted either without proof, or considered as having been before proved. In the former sense, it is synonymous with *axiom;* in the latter, with the phrase, *established principle*.

prism, *n.* A solid whose bases or ends are any similar, equal, and parallel plane figures, and whose sides are parallelograms. A prism of glass is one bounded by two equal and parallel triangular ends and three plain and well polished sides which meet in three parallel lines, running from the three angles of one end to the three angles of the other end.

product, *n.* In *arithmetic*, the amount of two or more numbers multiplied. Thus 5 x 7 = 35, the product. *Product* results from *multiplication*, as *sum* does from *addition*. 2. In *geometry*, the factum of two or more lines.

progression, *n.* In *mathematics*, regular or proportional advance in increase or decrease of numbers; continued proportion, arithmetical or geometrical. Continued arithmetical proportion, is when the terms increase or decrease by equal differences.

proportion, *n.* The comparative relation of any one thing to another. 2. The identity or similitude of two ratios. *Proportion* differs from *ratio*. 3. In *arithmetic*, a rule by which, when three numbers are given, a fourth number is found, which bears the same relation to the third as the second does to the first; or a fourth number is found, bearing the same relation to the second as the first does to the third. The former is called *direct*, and the latter, *inverse proportion*.

protractor, *n.* An instrument for laying down and measuring angles on paper with accuracy and dispatch, and by which the use of the line of chords is superseded. It is of various forms, semicircular, rectangular or circular.

pure, *a.* [L. *purus;* the Hebrew verb signifies to separate, free, clear.] Unmixed; separate from any other subject or from every thing foreign; as *pure* mathematics.

pyramid, *n.* A solid body standing on a triangular, square, or polygonal base, and terminating in a point at the top; or in geometry, a solid figure consisting of several triangles, whose bases are all in the same plane, and which have one common vertex. A *pyramid* is formed by the meeting of three or more planes at a point termed the apex.

quadratic, *a.* Square; denoting a square or pertaining to it. *Quadratic equation*, in algebra, an equation in which the unknown quantity is of two dimensions, or raised to the second power; or one in which the highest power of the unknown quantity is a square.

quadrilateral, *n.* A figure having four sides and four angles.

quantity, *n.* [Fr. *quantité;* It. *quantità;* Sp. *cantitad;* from L. *quantitas*, from *quantus*, how much, or as much as.] In *mathematics*, any thing which can be multiplied, divided or measured. Thus mathematics is called the science of quantity. In algebra, quantities are *known* and *unknown*. *Known quantities* are usually represented by the first letters of the alphabet, as *a, b, c,* and *unknown quantities* are expressed by the last letters, *x, y, z,* &c. Letters thus used to represent quantities are themselves called quantities. A simple quantity is expressed by one term, as $+ a$, or $- abc$; a compound is expressed by more terms than one, connected by the signs, + plus, or – minus, as $a + b$, or $a - b + c$. Quantities which have the sign + prefixed, are called *positive* or *affirmative;* those which have the sign – prefixed are called *negative*.

quotient, *n.* In *arithmetic*, the number resulting from the division of one number by another, and showing how often a less number is contained in a greater. Thus 3)12(4. Here 4 is the *quotient*, showing that 3 is contained 4 times in 12. Or *quotient* is an expression denoting a certain part of a unit; as $\frac{3}{4}$.

radical, *n.* *Radical quantities*, in algebra, quantities whose roots may be accurately expressed in numbers. The term is sometimes extended to all quantities under the radical sign. *Radical sign*, the sign $\sqrt{}$ placed before any quantity, denoting that its root is to be extracted.

radius, *n.* In *geometry*, a right line drawn or extending from the center of a circle to the periphery, and hence the semidiameter of the circle. In trigonometry, the radius is the whole sine, or sine of 90 degrees.

rate, *n.* The proportion or standard by which quantity or value is adjusted.

ratio, *n.* Proportion, or the relation of homogeneous things which determines the quantity of one from the quantity of another, without the intervention of a third. The relation which one quantity has to another of the same kind, as expressed by the quotient of the one divided by the other. Thus the ratio of 4 to 2 is $\frac{4}{2}$, or 2; and the ratio of 5 to 6 is $\frac{5}{6}$. This is *geometrical* ratio, which is that signified when the term is used without distinction; but arithmetical ratio is the *difference* between two quantities. Thus the arithmetical ratio of 2 to 6 is 4. *Ratio* respects magnitudes of the same kind only. One line may be compared with another line, but a line cannot be compared

with a superficies, and hence between a line and a superficies there can be no *ratio*.

reciprocal, *n*. The *reciprocal* of any quantity, is unity divided by that quantity. Thus the *reciprocal* of 4 is $\frac{1}{4}$.

rectangle, *n*. A right angled parallelogram. 2. In *arithmetic*, the product of two lines multiplied into each other.

reduction, *n*. In *arithmetic*, the bringing of numbers of different denominations into one denomination; as the *reduction* of pounds, ounces, pennyweights and grains to grains, or the *reduction* of grains to pounds; the *reduction* of days and hours to minutes, or of minutes to hours and days. The change of numbers of a higher denomination into a lower, as of pounds into pence or farthings, is called *reduction descending;* the change of numbers of a lower denomination into higher, as of cents into dimes, dollars or eagles, is called *reduction ascending*. Hence the rule for bringing sums of different denominations into one denomination, is called *reduction*. 2. In *algebra*, reduction of equations is the clearing of them of all superfluous quantities, bringing them to their lowest terms and separating the known from the unknown, till the unknown quantity alone is found on one side, and the known ones on the other.

remainder, *n*. Any thing left after the separation and removal of a part. 2. The sum that is left after subtraction or after any deduction.

rhombus, *n*. In *geometry*, an oblique angled parallelogram, or a quadrilateral figure whose sides are equal and parallel, but the angles unequal, two of the angles being obtuse and two acute. It consists of two equal and right cones united at the base.

root, *n*. In *arithmetic* and *algebra*, the root of any quantity is such a quantity as, when multiplied into itself a certain number of times, will exactly produce that quantity. Thus 2 is a root of 4, because when multiplied into itself, it exactly produces 4.

rule, *n*. In *arithmetic* and *algebra*, a determinate mode prescribed for performing any operation and producing a certain result.

science, *n*. [Fr. from L. *scientia*, from *scio*, to know; Sp. *ciencia;* It. *scienza. Scio* is probably a contracted word.] 1. In a general sense, knowledge, or certain knowledge; the comprehension or understanding of truth or facts by the mind. The *science* of God must be perfect. 2. In *philosophy*, a collection of the general principles or leading truths relating to any subject. *Pure* science, as the mathematics, is built on self-evident truths; but the term science is also applied to other subjects founded on generally acknowledged truths, as *metaphysics*; or on experiment and observation, as chemistry and *natural philosophy*; or even to an assemblage of the general principles of an art, as the science of *agriculture*; the science of *navigation*. *Arts* relate to practice, as painting and sculpture.

secant, *n*. 1. In *geometry*, a line that cuts another, or divides it into parts. The secant of a circle is a line drawn from the circumference on one side, to a point without the circumference on the other. In *trigonometry*, a secant is a right line drawn from the center of a circle, which, cutting the circumference, proceeds till it meets with a tangent to the same circle. 2. In *trigonometry*, the secant of an arc is a right line drawn from the center through one end of the arc, and terminated by a tangent drawn through the other end.

segment, *n*. In *geometry*, that part of the circle contained between a chord and an arch of that circle, or so much of the circle as is cut off by the chord.

series, *n*. In *arithmetic* and *algebra*, a number of terms in succession, increasing or diminishing in a certain ratio; as arithmetical *series* and geometrical *series*.

similar, *a*. Like; resembling; having a like form or appearance.

sine, *n*. In *geometry*, the right sine of an arch or arc, is a line drawn from one end of that arch, perpendicular to the radius drawn through the other end, and is always equal to half the chord of double the arch.

solid, *a*. Having all of the geometrical dimensions; cubic.

solution, *n*. In *algebra* and *geometry*, the answering of a question, or the resolving of a problem proposed.

speculative, *a*. [Fr. *speculatif;* It. *speculativo*.] 1. Given to speculation; contemplative; *applied to persons*. 2. Formed by speculation; theoretical; ideal; not verified by fact, experiment or practice; as a scheme merely *speculative*.

sphere, *n*. In *geometry*, a solid body contained under a single surface, which in every part is equally distant from a point called its center.

square, *n*. A figure having four equal sides and four right angles.

substitution, *n*. The act of putting one person or thing in the place of another to supply its place; as the *substitution* of an agent, attorney or representative to act for one in his absence; the *substitution* of bank notes for gold and silver, as a circulating medium.

subtract, *v.t.* To withdraw or take a part from the rest; to deduct. *Subtract* 5 from 9, and the remainder is 4.

subtraction, *n.* The act or operation of taking a part from the rest. 2. In *arithmetic*, the taking of a lesser number from a greater of the same kind or denomination; an operation by which is found the difference between two sums.

subtrahend, *n.* In *arithmetic*, the sum or number to be subtracted or taken from another.

sum, *n.* The aggregate of two or more numbers, magnitudes, quantities or particulars; the amount or whole of any number of individuals or particulars added. The *sum* of 5 and 7 is 12.

sum, *v.t.* To add particulars into one whole; to collect two or more particular numbers into one number; to cast up; usually followed by *up*, but it is superfluous. Custom enables a man to *sum up* a long column of figures with surprising facility and correctness.

supplement, *n.* In *trigonometry*, the quantity by which an arc or an angle falls short of 180 degrees or a semicircle.

surd, *n.* In *algebra*, a quantity whose root cannot be exactly expressed in numbers. Thus 2 is a surd number, because there is no number which multiplied into itself, will exactly produce 2.

surface, *n.* The exterior part of any thing that has length and breadth; one of the limits that terminates a solid; the superficies; outside; as the *surface* of the earth; the *surface* of the sea; the *surface* of a diamond; the *surface* of the body; the *surface* of a cylinder; an even or an uneven *surface;* a smooth or rough *surface;* a spherical *surface*.

symmetrical, *a.* Proportional in its parts; having its parts in due proportion, as to dimensions; as a *symmetrical* body or building.

synthesis, *n.* The putting of two or more things together.

tangent, *n.* In *geometry*, a right line which touches a curve, but which when produced, does not cut it. In *trigonometry*, the tangent of an arc, is a right line touching the arc at one extremity, and terminated by a secant passing through the other extremity.

tetrahedron, *n.* In *geometry*, a figure comprehended under four equilateral and equal triangles.

theorem, *n.* 1. In *mathematics*, a proposition which terminates in theory, and which considers the properties of things already made or done; or it is a speculative proposition deduced from several definitions compared together. A theorem is a proposition to be proved by a chain of reasoning. A theorem is something to be *proved;* a problem is something to be *done*. 2. In *algebra* or *analysis*, it is sometimes used to denote a rule, particularly when that rule is expressed by symbols.

total, *n.* The whole; the whole sum or amount. These sums added, make the grand *total* of five millions.

transpose, *v.t.* 1. To change the place or order of things by putting each in the place of the other; as, to *transpose* letters, words or propositions. 2. In *algebra*, to bring any term of an equation over to the other side. Thus if $a + b = c$, and we make $a = c - b$, then b is said to be *transposed*.

trapezoid, *n.* An irregular solid figure having four sides, no two of which are parallel to each other; also, a plane four sided figure having two of the opposite sides parallel to each other.

triangle, *n.* In *geometry*, a figure bounded by three lines, and containing three angles. The three angles of a triangle are equal to two right angles, or the number of degrees in a semicircle.

trigonometry, *n.* [Gr. a triangle and to measure.] The measuring of triangles; the science of determining the sides and angles of triangles, by means of certain parts which are given. When this science is applied to the solution of plane triangles, it is called *plane* trigonometry; when its application is to spherical triangles, it is called *spherical* trigonometry.

trinomial, *a.* In *mathematics*, a *trinomial* root is a root consisting of three parts, connected by the signs + or –. Thus $x + y + z$, or $a + b - c$.

trinomial, *n.* A root of three terms or parts.

unit, *n.* 1. One; a word which denotes a single thing or person; the least whole number. 2. In *mathematics*, any known determinate quantity, by the constant repetition of which, any other quantity of the same kind is measured.

variable, *n.* In *mathematics*, a quantity which is in a state of continual increase or decrease. The indefinitely small quantity by which a variable is continually increased or diminished, is called its *differential*, and the method of finding these quantities, the *differential calculus*.

vertex, *n.* The top of a hill or other thing; the point of a cone, pyramid, angle or figure; the pole of a glass, in optics. The vertex of a curve, is the point from which the diameter is drawn, or the intersection of the diameter and the curve.

Biblical Terms Used for Measurement

Diverse and deceitful weights are shamefully vile and abhorrent
to the Lord, and false scales are not good.
(Proverbs 20:23, Amplified)

The chart below lists the units of measure common in Old and New Testament times and their approximate modern equivalences.

OLD TESTAMENT			NEW TESTAMENT		
Unit	US System (approx.)	Metric System (approx.)	Unit	US System (approx.)	Metric System (approx.)
Linear Measurement					
Finger	¾ in	1.85 cm	Cubit	1 ft 6 in	44.4 cm
Palm	3 in	7.4 cm	Long cubit	1 ft 9 in	52.5 cm
Span	8 ¾ in	26.2 cm	Fathom	5 ft 10 in	1.78 m
Cubit	1 ft 6 in	44.4 cm	Stade	600 ft	178 m
Royal cubit	1 ft 9 in	52.5 cm	Roman Mile	4857.6 ft	1482 m
Dry Measurement					
Kab	2 1/3 pt	1.2 L	Litra (Gr)	1 lb	.45 Kg
Omer	2 qt	2.2 L			
Seah	1/5 bu	7.33 L			
Ephah	3/5 bu	22 L	Modion (Gr)	15 lbs	6.8 Kg
Homer	6 ¼ bu	220 L			
Liquid Measurement					
Log	1/3 qt	0.3 L	Xestes (Gr)	1 pt	0.54 L
Hin	4 qt	3.66 L			
Bath	5 ½ gal	22 L			
Homer	58 gal	220 L	Choinix (Gr)	1 qt	1.08 L

Biblical Terms Relating to the Components of Mathematics

He counts the number of the stars; He calls them all by name.
Great is our Lord, and mighty in power; His understanding is infinite.
(Psalm 147:4–5, NKJV)

Component	Term	Reference	Scripture
Measurement	Acre	1 Sam. 14:14	"Jonathan . . . killed some twenty men in an area of about half an acre."
Measurement	Bushel	Mark 4:21	"Is a lamp brought in to be put under a bushel?" (RSV)
Measurement	Cubit	Gen. 6:15	"[T]he length of the ark three hundred cubits, its breadth fifty cubits, and its height thirty cubits." (NASB)
Measurement	Day/Night	Gen. 1:14	"And God said, Let there be lights in the firmament of the heaven to divide the day from the night."
Measurement	Debt	Matt. 18:27	"[T]he lord of that servant released him and forgave him the debt." (RSV)
Notation	Deed	Jer. 32:10	"I signed and sealed the deed, had it witnessed, and weighed out the silver on the scales."
Measurement	Estimation	Lev. 27:25	"And all thy estimations shall be according to the shekel of the sanctuary."
Measurement	Fathom	Acts 27:28	"And sounded, and found it twenty fathoms."
Measurement	Fee	Num. 22:7	"So the elders . . . departed with the fees for divination in their hand." (NASB)
Measurement	Finger	Jer. 52:21	"[T]he height of each pillar was eighteen cubits, and it was twelve cubits in circumference and four fingers in thickness, and hollow." (NASB)
Measurement	Gallon	John 2:6	"Now six stone water jars were standing there, . . . each holding twenty or thirty gallons." (RSV)
Measurement	Gerah	Lev. 27:25	"[T]wenty gerahs shall be the shekel."
Numbers	Half	Mark 6:23	"I will give you, even half of my kingdom." (RSV)
Measurement	Handbreadth	Ex. 25:25	"[M]ake around it a rim a handbreadth wide."
Measurement	Hin	Ezek. 4:11	You shall drink water by measure also, about one quart or the sixth part of a hin; you shall drink at a fixed time each day. (Amplified)

Component	Term	Reference	Scripture
Measurement	Interest	Deut. 23:19	"You shall not lend on interest to your brother." (Amplified)
Measurement	Line, Plane,	Isa. 44:13	"The carpenter stretches out a line; . . . he fashions [an idol] with planes, and marks it out with the compasses." (Amplified)
Measurement	Loans	Deut. 23:20	"You may lend on interest to a foreigner." (Amplified)
Measurement	Log	Lev. 14:12	"[W]ith the log of oil, and present them as a wave offering before the LORD." (NASB)
Operations	Market	John 2:16	"How dare you turn my Father's house into a market!"
Measurement	Measure	Deut. 25:14	"You shall not have in your house differing measures, a large and a small." (NASB)
Measurement	Mile	John 11:18–19	"Bethany was near Jerusalem, about two miles off." (RSV)
Measurement	Mina	1 Kings 10:17	"[U]sing three minas of gold on each shield." (NASB)
Measurement	Money	1 Tim. 6:10	"For the love of money is the root of all evil."
Numbers	Number	Ex. 1:5	"All the persons who came from . . . Jacob were seventy in number." (NASB)
Measurement	Plumb line	Amos 7:7	"[T]he Lord stood upon a wall with a plumb line, with a plumb line in His hand." (Amplified)
Numbers	Thousand	Ps. 105:8	"He has remembered His covenant forever, . . . to a thousand generations." (NASB)
Measurement	Time	Matt. 25:13	"Watch therefore, for you know neither the day nor the hour." (RSV)
Measurement	Wages	Deut. 24:15	"You shall give him his wages on his day before the sun sets." (NASB)
Measurement	Wealth	Mark 10:23	"How hard it will be for those who have riches to enter the kingdom of God!" (RSV)
Measurement	Weight	Prov. 20:23	"Differing weights are an abomination to the LORD, And a false scale is not good." (NASB)
Notation	Writing	Ex. 32:16	"[A]nd the writing was the writing of God engraved on the tablets." (NKJV)

Addition Table

83 Addition Facts Reduced to 47 Single-Digit Addition Facts

47 Single-Digit Addition Facts Reduced to 19 Sums

0	**1**	2	3	4	**5**	6	7	8	9
0+0=0	0+1=1	1+1=2	1+2=3	1+3=4	**1+4=5**	**1+5=6**	1+6=7	1+7=8	1+8=9
				2+2=4	**2+3=5**	2+4=6	**2+5=7**	2+6=8	2+7=9
						3+3=6	3+4=7	**3+5=8**	3+6=9
								4+4=8	**4+5=9**

10	11	12	13	14	15	16	17	18
1+9=10	1+10=11	1+11=12	1+12=13	1+13=14	1+14=15	1+15=16	1+16=17	1+17=18
2+8=10	2+9=11	2+10=12	2+11=13	2+12=14	2+13=15	2+14=16	2+15=17	2+16=18
3+7=10	3+8=11	3+9=12	3+10=13	3+11=14	3+12=15	3+13=16	3+14=17	3+15=18
4+6=10	4+7=11	4+8=12	4+9=13	4+10=14	4+11=15	4+12=16	4+13=17	4+14=18
5+5=10	5+6=11	5+7=12	5+8=13	5+9=14	5+10=15	5+11=16	5+12=17	5+13=18
		6+6=12	6+7=13	6+8=14	6+9=15	6+10=16	6+11=17	6+12=18
				7+7=14	7+8=15	7+9=16	7+10=17	7+11=18
						8+8=16	8+9=17	8+10=18
								9+9=18

Coded in **bold** are the number combinations, which, together with the combinations in reverse (i.e., 1+4=5 and 4+1=5), must be learned first.

Coded in ***bold italics*** are the number combinations to be learned only after the first combinations are mastered.

Shaded are the single-digit number combinations essential for success in addition that must be learned through usage, recitation, and drill.

In plain type are the number combinations that have already been learned as single-digit facts above.

Analysis of 156 Multiplication Facts Reduced to 66 Facts

0x0=0	*1x0=0*	*2x0=0*	*3x0=0*	*4x0=0*	*5x0=0*	*6x0=0*	*7x0=0*	*8x0=0*	*9x0=0*	*10x0=0*	*11x0=0*	*12x0=0*
0x1=0	**1x1=1**	**2x1=2**	**3x1=3**	**4x1=4**	**5x1=5**	**6x1=6**	**7x1=7**	**8x1=8**	**9x1=9**	**10x1=10**	**11x1=11**	**12x1=12**
0x2=0	**1x2=2**	2x2=4	3x2=6	4x2=8	5x2=10	6x2=12	7x2=14	8x2=16	9x2=18	10x2=20	11x2=22	12x2=24
0x3=0	**1x3=3**	2x3=6	3x3=9	4x3=12	5x3=15	6x3=18	7x3=21	8x3=24	9x3=27	10x3=30	11x3=33	12x3=36
0x4=0	**1x4=4**	2x4=8	3x4=12	4x4=16	5x4=20	6x4=24	7x4=28	8x4=32	9x4=36	10x4=40	11x4=44	12x4=48
0x5=0	**1x5=5**	2x5=10	3x5=15	4x5=20	5x5=25	6x5=30	7x5=35	8x5=40	9x5=45	10x5=50	11x5=55	12x5=60
0x6=0	**1x6=6**	2x6=12	3x6=18	4x6=24	5x6=30	6x6=36	7x6=42	8x6=48	9x6=54	10x6=60	11x6=66	12x6=72
0x7=0	**1x7=7**	2x7=14	3x7=21	4x7=28	5x7=35	6x7=42	7x7=49	8x7=56	9x7=63	10x7=70	11x7=77	12x7=84
0x8=0	**1x8=8**	2x8=16	3x8=24	4x8=32	5x8=40	6x8=48	7x8=56	8x8=64	9x8=72	10x8=80	11x8=88	12x8=96
0x9=0	**1x9=9**	2x9=18	3x9=27	4x9=36	5x9=45	6x9=54	7x9=63	8x9=72	9x9=81	10x9=90	11x9=99	12x9=108
0x10=0	**1x10=10**	2x10=20	3x10=30	4x10=40	5x10=50	6x10=60	7x10=70	8x10=80	9x10=90	10x10=100	11x10=110	12x10=120
0x11=0	**1x11=11**	2x11=22	3x11=33	4x11=44	5x11=55	6x11=66	7x11=77	8x11=88	9x11=99	10x11=110	11x11=121	12x11=132
0x12=0	**1x12=12**	2x12=24	3x12=36	4x12=48	5x12=60	6x12=72	7x12=84	8x12=96	9x12=108	10x12=120	11x12=132	12x12=144

Coded in *italics* are facts not requiring memorization but a rule instead. (Rule: any number multiplied by zero equals zero.)

Coded in **bold** are facts not requiring memorization but a rule instead. (Rule: a number multiplied by one equals itself.)

Underlined are facts that are easily remembered because they are perfect squares.

Shaded are the combinations that must be memorized in order to be successful in multiplication.

In plain type are facts appearing elsewhere on the table but with their multipliers and multiplicands transposed.

May be duplicated.

Subtraction Table

45 Single-Digit Subtraction Facts

1	2	3	4	5	6	7	8	9
1-1=0	2-1=1	3-1=2	4-1=3	***5-1=4***	6-1=5	7-1=6	8-1=7	9-1=8
	2-2=0	3-2=1	4-2=2	***5-2=3***	6-2=4	7-2=5	8-2=6	9-2=7
		3-3=0	4-3=1	***5-3=2***	6-3=3	7-3=4	8-3=5	9-3=6
			4-4=0	***5-4=1***	6-4=2	7-4=3	8-4=4	9-4=5
				5-5=0	***6-5=1***	***7-5=2***	***8-5=3***	***9-5=4***
					6-6=0	7-6=1	8-6=2	9-6=3
						7-7=0	8-7=1	9-7=2
							8-8=0	9-8=1
								9-9=0

These single-digit number combinations must be learned through usage, recitation, and drill in order to achieve success in subtraction.

Those facts in ***boldface italics*** should be learned first.

People Who Impacted History: John Napier, 1550–1617

Providential Setting	Spheres of Influence	Character	Contributions
1. European Reformation 2. Scotland: • Born in 1550, in Merchiston Castle, Edinburgh • Birth of the Presbyterian Church (1560) "the Covenanters" 3. Lived as an adult in a castle he had built at Gartness; ran his estates; dabbled in agriculture. 4. Died in 1617 and is buried in St. Cuthbert's Church in Edinburgh. 5. Civil sphere struggles with Scottish commitment to Calvinistic Presbyterianism's political strife with England. 6. Monarchs during his life: • Mary, Queen of Scots • James I of England and Scotland • Charles I • Charles II • James II 7. Contemporaries: John Knox John Calvin William Shakespeare The Pilgrims	1. Father: Archibald Napier • Justice deputy • Knighted in 1565 • Landowner • Master of the Mint 1582 2. Mother: Janet Bothwell, sister of the Bishop of Orkney 3. Education (*T&L*, 170–171): • Entered St. Andrew's University at the age of 13; left two years later without a degree. • Continued his studies of mathematics and classical literature in Europe. 4. Knighted in 1565. 5. Married in 1572; had one son and one daughter; his first wife died shortly thereafter; remarried and had five sons and five daughters. 6. The writings of: • John Knox • John Calvin	1. Philosopher 2. Mathematician 3. Religious 4. Man of integrity 5. Loyal 6. Humble 7. Considerate of others 8. Man of vision 9. Lived by Biblical principles 10. Statesman 11. Scholar; mathematics was only a hobby 12. Precise and accurate 13. Lover of numbers 14. Lover of theology 15. Genius intellect	1. Invented logarithms, which greatly assisted in arithmetic calculations. His logarithms were the basis for the invention of the slide rule and laid the foundation for Kepler's and Newton's work in mathematics. 2. Invented a tool called Napier's Bones, which were multiplication tables inscribed on strips of wood or bone and used for mechanically multiplying, dividing, and taking square roots and cube roots. 3. Invented: the decimal point; a mnemonic for formulas used in solving spherical triangles; and two formulas known as Napier's analogies used in solving spherical triangles. Found exponential expressions for trigonometric functions. Introduced decimal notation for fractions. 4. Authored: • *Plaine Discovery of the Whole Revelation of St. John:* apocalyptic writings of great fascination. Napier believed that the symbols it contained were mathematical, which could be discovered with reason. • *Mirifici logarithmorum canonis descriptio,* 1614; • *Rabdologie,* 1617: described a method of multiplication using rods with numbers etched on them, which was the forerunner of the mechanical calculator. 5. Napier University in Scotland is named after him.

Sample Teacher Notebook Pages

A Summary of the Operation of Addition

The first operation studied in mathematics is addition. The purpose of this section is to identify the principles and rules pertaining to this operation arithmetically.

Definition: addition, n. [L. additio, from addo.]

In arithmetic, the uniting of two or more numbers in one sum; also the rule or branch of arithmetic which treats of adding numbers. Simple addition is the joining of sums of the same denomination, as pounds to pounds, dollars to dollars. Compound addition is the joining of sums of different denominations, as dollars and cents.

add, v. t. [L. addo, from ad and do, to give.]

1. To set or put together, join, or unite, as, one thing or sum to another, in an aggregate; as, add three to four, the sum is seven.
2. To increase number.

Terms: Addend—the number to be added or joined to another

Sum or total—the result of the uniting of two or more like numbers.

Biblical Usage: To "add to" is used in Scripture as equivalent to give, bestow upon, and increase. (Luke 17:5) In general, when used of things, "add" implies a principal thing to which a smaller is to be annexed as a part of the whole sum, mass, or number.

Result: A sum or amount

Principles:

1. Only numbers of like kind (numbers having the same unit of measure) can be added.
2. The sum, or whole, is equal to all the units of all the parts.
3. The sum has the same unit of measure as the numbers being added.
4. Numbers in the same order, and only such, can be added directly.
5. The sum, or result of addition, is the same in whatever order the addends are added.

Rules:

1. Write the numbers to be added aligning figures of the same order (e.g., units, tens, hundreds) in the same column, and draw a line directly beneath the column(s).
2. Beginning with the column of numerals farthest to the right, add each numeral within the column and record the total under the column added, and carry the tens, if any, to the next column to the left. Continue to add any remaining columns, separately recording their sums and carrying to the column to the left, if necessary, until the last column is added and the last sum is recorded.

Methods of Proof:

1. Add the given numbers in an arrangement different than originally used (e.g., upward instead of downward).
2. Group the given numbers into twos or threes. Add these groups separately and record the subtotals of these groupings. Upon completion, add the subtotals to arrive at the grand total.
3. Cast out nines.

A Summary of the Operation of Multiplication

The purpose of this section is to identify the principles and rules pertaining to this operation applied arithmetically.

Definition: multiplication, n. [L. multiplicatio.]

In arithmetic, a rule or operation by which any given number may be increased according to any number of times proposed. Thus 10 multiplied by 5 is increased to 50.

multiply, v. t. [L. multiplico; multus, many, and plico, to fold or double.]

1. To increase in number; to make more by natural generation or production, or by addition.
2. In arithmetic, to increase any given number as many times as there are units in any other given number. Thus 7 x 8 = 56, that is, 7 multiplied by 8 produces the number 56.

Terms: multiplicand—the number to be multiplied by another, which is called the multiplier
multiplier—the number by which another is multiplied
product—the result

Biblical Usage: To "multiply" is used in Scripture as equivalent to rapid increase, to superabound. (2 Corinthians 9:10; Hebrews 6:14)

Result: A product

Principles:

1. The multiplicand may be either concrete (has a definite unit of measure) or abstract (no unit of measure).
2. The multiplier must always be an abstract number.
3. The product has the same unit of measure as the multiplicand.
4. The partial products are the same unit of measure as the multiplicand.
5. The sum of the partial products is equal to the combined or final product.
6. The number of partial products is equal to the number of digits in the multiplier.

Rules:

1. Write the multiplier beneath the multiplicand, being sure to place numerals of the same order into the same column, and draw a line beneath the multiplier after placing the sign of multiplication (x)—the government of the problem—in front of the multiplier.
2. Multiply each figure of the multiplicand by each figure of the multiplier, beginning with the units figure, and record the first figure of the partial product under that figure of the multiplier. Upon completion, proceed one column to the left, and repeat the above process until all figures of the multiplicand have been multiplied by all the figures contained in the multiplier.
3. Add the partial products together; their sum will be the result of the operation of the product.

Methods of Proof:

1. Multiply the multiplier by the multiplicand. If the original product is correct, it will equal the second product obtained.
2. Divide the product by the multiplier to obtain the original multiplicand.
3. Cast out nines.

A Summary of the Operation of Subtraction

One of the first operations studied in mathematics is subtraction. The purpose of this section is to identify the principles and rules pertaining to this operation applied to arithmetic.

Definition: subtraction, n. [L. subtractio.]

In arithmetic, the taking of a lesser number from a greater of the same kind or denomination; an operation by which is found the difference between two sums.

subtract, v. t. [L. subtraho, subtractus; sub and traho, to draw.]

To withdraw or take a part from the rest; to deduct. Subtract 5 from 9, and the remainder is 4.

Terms: minuend—the larger number

subtrahend—the smaller number being taken from the minuend

remainder or difference—the amount remaining

Biblical Usage: To "subtract" is used in Scripture as equivalent to deduct or diminish. Deuteronomy 4:2

In general, when used of things, "subtract" implies a principal thing from which a smaller is to be taken.

Result: A difference, a remainder

Principles:
1. Only numbers of like kind (numbers having the same unit of measure) can be subtracted.
2. The difference is the same in kind as the minuend and subtrahend.
3. The difference equals the minuend minus the subtrahend.
4. The minuend equals the difference plus the subtrahend.
5. The subtrahend equals the minuend minus the difference.

Rules:
1. Write the smaller of the two numbers under the greater number by aligning numerals of the same denomination under each other, place the subtraction sign (-)—the sign which governs the operation—in front of the subtrahend, and draw a line beneath the subtrahend.
2. Begin to subtract each figure from the one above it, placing the remainder beneath the line. Begin with the column of numerals farthest to the right and proceed to the left.
3. If any figure exceeds the one above it, borrow one unit from the column to the left of that numeral and increase the minuend by the amount borrowed to the right, and decrease by one unit the minuend number in the column to the left. Proceed to subtract using the newly-acquired minuend and record the difference under the column being subtracted until all numerals have been subtracted.

Method of Proof:
1. Add the remainder (difference) to the subtrahend. If the work is correct, this sum will be equal to the minuend.
2. Cast out nines.

A Summary of the Operation of Division

The purpose of this section is to identify the principles and rules pertaining to this operation.

Definition: division, n. [L. divisio, from divido, divisi.]
In arithmetic, the dividing of a number or quantity into any parts assigned; or the rule by which is found how many times one number is contained in another.
divide, v. t. [L. divido; di or dis and iduo, that is, viduo, to part.]
1. To part or separate an entire thing; to part a thing into two or more pieces.
2. To distribute; to separate and bestow in parts or shares.

Terms: divisor–the number by which the dividend is divided
dividend–the number to be divided into equal parts
quotient–the number resulting from the division of one number by another, and showing how often a less number is contained in a greater one

Biblical Usage: To "divide" is used in Scripture as equivalent to separate into parts. (Luke 15:12; 1 Cor. 12:11; 1 Kings 3:25)

Result: A quotient

Principles:
1. When the divisor and dividend have the same unit of measure, the quotient is abstract.
2. When the divisor is an abstract number, the quotient will have the same unit of measure as the dividend.
3. The unit of measure of the remainder is the same as that of the dividend.
4. The product of the quotient multiplied by the divisor, plus any remainder, is equal to the dividend.

Rules:
1. Write the divisor to the left of the symbol for division $\overline{)\quad}$ and the dividend inside the symbol.
2. Determine how often the divisor is contained in the first figure or figures of the dividend, and record the answer above the dividend as the quotient.
3. Multiply this quotient by the divisor, and write the product under that part of the dividend from which it was obtained.
4. Subtract this product from the dividend above it, and record the remainder below the product. To this remainder, bring down the next figure of the dividend, and find how often the divisor is contained in it as before, until all the figures of the dividend are brought down.
5. If the number formed after a figure is brought down is too small to contain the divisor, a zero must be placed in the quotient and another figure from the dividend brought down to allow the division process to continue.
6. When there is a final remainder after the last division, form a fraction by placing the remainder into the numerator position and the divisor into the denominator position, and attach this fraction to the quotient already obtained.

Methods of Proof:
1. Multiply the quotient by the given divisor and to the resulting product add the remainder, if any. If the original work is correct, the new sum will be equal to the original dividend.
2. Cast out nines.

Resources

TEXTBOOKS

Cotter, Joan. *RightStart™; Activities for Learning*, (K–4th Grade). Joan Cotter. Hutchinson, MN, 2001.

Foerster, Paul A. *Algebra 1: Expressions, Equations, and Applications*. Upper Saddle River, NJ: Prentice Hall, 1999.

Foerster, Paul A. *Algebra 2: Algebra and Trigonometry: Functions and Applications*. Upper Saddle River, NJ: Prentice Hall, 1999.

Holliday, Cuevas, Moore-Harris, Carter, Marks, Casey, Day, and Hayek. *Algebra 1*. New York: Glencoe MGraw-Hill, 2005.

Larson, Hostetler, and Edwards. *Calculus with Analytic Geometry*, 6th Ed. Boston, MA: Houghton Mifflin, 1998.

Larson. *Complete Solutions Guide to Accompany Calculus*, 6th Ed. Boston, MA: Houghton Mifflin, 1998.

Larson, Boswell, and Stiff. *Geometry: Applying, Reasoning, Measuring*. Geneva, IL: Houghton Mifflin, 2001.

Larson, Hostetler, and Edwards. *Precalculus with Limits: A Graphing Approach*, 3rd Ed. Boston, MA: Houghton Mifflin, 2001.

Larson, Hostetler, and Edwards. *Study and Solutions Guide [for Precalculus with Limits: A Graphing Approach]*. Boston, MA: Houghton Mifflin, 2001.

Malloy, Price, Sloan, and Willard. *Pre-Algebra*. New York: Glencoe McGraw-Hill, 2005.

Ray, Joseph. *Ray's™ New Higher Arithmetic* (Grades 6–7). Milford, MI: Mott Media, Inc., 1985.

Ray, Joseph. *Ray's™ New Practical Arithmetic* (Grade 5). Milford, MI: Mott Media, Inc., 1985.

CURRICULUM ENRICHMENT

Barrow, John D. *Pi in the Sky: Counting, Thinking and Being*. Oxford, Great Britain: Clarendon Press, Oxford U, 1992.

Bell, E. T. *Men of Mathematics*. New York: Simon & Schuster, 1965.

Bennett, William J., Chester E. Finn, Jr., and John T. E. Cribb, Jr. *The Educated Child: A Parent's Guide from Preschool through Eighth Grade*. New York: The Free Press, 1999.

Block, John. *Bible Math Labs*. HC 79 Box 46, Gothenburg, NE 69138, 1996.

Bowditch, Nathaniel. *American Practical Navigator: An Epitome of Navigation and Nautical*. 1861, 1938 revised edition.

Boyer, Carl B. *A History of Mathematics*. New York: John Wiley & Sons, Inc., 1991.

Dordt College Press. *Bibliography of Christianity and Mathematics (1910–1983)*. Sioux Center, IA: Dordt College Press, 1983.

Dunham, William. *Journey through Genius*. New York: Penguin Press, 1991.

Grolier Interactive, Inc. *Grolier Multimedia Encyclopedia*. Novato, CA: Grolier Interactive, Inc., 1997.

Grun, Bernard. *The Timetables of History*. New York: Touchstone, Simon & Schuster, 1991.

Guillen, Michael. *Five Equations That Changed the World: The Power and Poetry of Mathematics*. New York: Hyperion, 1995.

Holton, Jean Laity. *Geometry: A New Way of Looking at Space*. New York: Weybright & Talley, 1971.

Kramer, Edna E. *The Nature and Growth of Modern Mathematics*. Princeton, NJ: Princeton University Press, 1982.

Longmans, Ed. *Napier: Tercentenary Memorial Volume*. Royal Society of Edinburgh: Green and Co., 1915.

Mullis, Ina V.S. et al. *NAEP 1992 Mathematics Report Card for the Nation and States*. Washington, D.C.: National Center for Education Statistics, Report #23-STOZ, 1993.

Morris, Henry M. *The Remarkable Record of Job: The Ancient Wisdom, Scientific Accuracy, and Life-changing Message of an Amazing Book*. Grand Rapids, MI: Baker Book House, 1988.

Napier, Mark. *The Memoirs of John Napier of Merchiston: His Lineage, Life, and Times with a History of the Invention of Logarithms*. Edinburgh: William Blackwood, and London: Thomas Cadell, 1834.

Napier, P. *A Difficult Country: The Napiers in Scotland*. London, UK: Michael. Joseph Publishers, 1972.

National Research Council. *Everybody Counts: A Report to the Nation on the Future of Mathematics Education.* Washington, D.C.: National Academy Press, 1989.

Newman, John Henry Cardinal. *The Scope and Nature of University Education.* New York: E. P. Dutton, 1958.

Nickel, James. *Mathematics: Is God Silent?* Vallecito, CA: Ross House Books, expanded ed. 2001.

North, Gary, Ed. "Essays in the Van Til Perspective," *Foundations of Scholarship.* Vallecito, CA: Ross House Books, 1976.

Paulos, John A. *Innumeracy.* New York: Vintage, 1990. *Beyond Innumeracy.* New York: Vintage, 1992.

Paulos, John A. *A Mathematician Reads the Newspaper.* New York: Vintage, 1996.

Polloway, E. and T. Smith. *Language Instruction for Students with Disabilities,* 2nd Ed. Denver, CO: Love Publishing Co., 1992.

Schaeffer, Francis A. *How Should We Then Live? The Rise and Decline of Western Thought and Culture.* Westchester, IL: Crossway Books, 1976.

Schroeder, Gerald. *Genesis and the Big Bang.* New York: Bantam Books, 1990, 1992.

Sebranek, Meyer, and Kemper. *Write for College.* Wilmington, MA: Houghton Mifflin Co., 1997.

Springer. *Mathematical Intelligencer,* New York: Springer, Springer-Verlag, New York, Inc., quarterly.

United States Government Printing Office. *Astronomy.* Washington, D.C.: United States Government Printing Office, annual.

World Book, Inc. *The World Book Encyclopedia.* Chicago, IL: World Book, Inc., annual.

INTERNET RESOURCES

American Mathematics Association. *American Mathematical Monthly.* American Mathematics Association, annual. Order from the MAA Service Center at 800-331-1622, 301-617-7800, e-mail maaservice@maa.org.

Center of Excellence for Science and Mathematics Education (CESME) Located at the University of Tennessee at Martin in Martin, Tennessee. The mission of CESME is to encourage and support the improvement of science and mathematics education at all levels. The purpose of this Website is to serve as a resource for teachers who are looking for ways to improve their science or mathematics teaching.

Cut-the-Knot An interactive column using Java applets. It contains numerous problem-solving applications and mathematical puzzles. www.cut-the-knot.com/ctk/index.html

Eisenhower National Clearinghouse Mission is to identify effective curriculum resources, create high-quality professional development materials, and disseminate useful information and products to improve K–12 mathematics and science teaching and learning. www.enc.org

Manipula Math with Java site contains over one hundred graphical JAVA applets that demonstrate mathematical concepts (elementary to calculus). www.ies.co.jp/math/java

Math Archives One of the most comprehensive Web resource sites. Teaching material, math-related sites, journals and magazines, government institutions, societies and colleges, and math departments. This site is an excellent guide to finding mathematics-related Internet resources. It includes links to lesson plans, software, topics in mathematics, contests, and much more. www.archives.math.utk.edu/k12.html

The Math Forum—An Online Math Education Community Center The goal is to build an online community of teachers, students, researchers, parents, educators, and citizens who have an interest in math and math education, by encouraging communication throughout the mathematical community, making math-related Web resources more accessible, providing high-quality math and math education content, and offering model interactive projects. www.forum.swarthmore.edu

Math Homework Help In addition to providing homework help for a fee, this site has a math dictionary, a list of various formulas for high school mathematics (including trig identities and geometry formulas), postulates, and theorems and practice problems from algebra. This site includes a "Chronology of Mathematics" timeline. www.users.adelphia.net/~mathhomeworkhelp

Math 2 Web site Contains helpful tables for theorems, proofs, tables, identities, and graphs; general math: number notation and multiplication tables; algebra: basic identities, polynomials, exponents, algebra, and graphs; geometry: areas, volumes, and surface areas; trigonometry: identities, tables, hyperbolics, and trig graphs; calculus: integrals, derivatives, advanced topics, and Fourier Series Transforms; miscellaneous: constants, vectors, complexity, and graphs. www.math2.com

Mathematically Correct Devoted to the concerns raised by parents and scientists about the invasion of our schools by the New-New Math and the need to restore basic skills to math education. "Mathematically Correct is the informal, nationwide organization that fights the Establishment on behalf of sanity and quality in math education." www.ourworld.compuserve.com/homepages/mathman/

Mathematics Glossary—Middle Years Definitions included are those used in the Saskatchewan Education document "Mathematics 6–9: A Curriculum Guide for the Middle Level." Various mathematics dictionaries may differ. These definitions are designed to be meaningful to mid-level mathematics teachers. www.mathcentral.uregina.ca

New York Times Lesson Archives Site contains numerous mathematics activities based on current events. www.nytimes.com/learning/teachers/lessons/mathematics.html

NASA Math Activities for K–12 Teachers In December, 1997, NASA Dryden Flight Research Center funded Dan Biezad, Professor of Aerospace Engineering, and Robin Ward, Assistant Professor of Mathematics, both of California Polytechnic State University, San Luis Obispo, to develop materials for K–12 teachers based on aeronautical themes and NASA projects. One major goal of this project was to make the learning of mathematics more engaging and realistic for students by using real-world applications.

The Role of Story Problems in Transition from Arithmetic to Algebra Project to provide electronic access to a large collection of story problems from many cultures and historical periods. www.mcs.open.ac.uk/cme/Arith2Alg.html

ASSOCIATIONS AND ORGANIZATIONS

AIMS Education Foundation Acronym for "Activities Integrating Mathematics and Science." Its mission is to enrich the education of students in K–9 through hands-on activities that integrate mathematics, science, and other disciplines. AIMS implements the recommendations put forth in reform documents such as "Science for All Americans" (American Association for the Advancement of Science), "Curriculum and Evaluation Standards for School Mathematics" (National Council of Teachers of Mathematics), and by the National Research Council's Standards. AIMS Education Foundation, 1595 S. Chestnut Ave, Fresno, California 93702. Toll-free: 1-888-SEE-AIMS, www.aimsedu.org

Association of Teachers of Mathematics (ATM) Relates mathematical education more closely to the powers and needs of the learner. The Association was formed in 1950 and has about 4000 members, mainly teachers in primary and secondary schools. It is a registered charity and re-invests all profits back into mathematics education. The ATM provides opportunities to bring together all concerned with mathematical education for all age ranges. It supports local branches, local and national working groups, informal support networks, courses and conferences.: www.atm.org.uk

National Council of Teachers of Mathematics (NCTM) Founded in 1920 as a nonprofit professional and educational association, the largest organization dedicated to the improvement of mathematics education and to meeting the needs of teachers of mathematics. NCTM Headquarters Office, 1906 Association Drive, Reston, Virginia 20191-9988, (703) 620-9840, fax: (703) 476-2970. www.nctm.org/about/beliefs.html

PRINCIPLE APPROACH® RESOURCES AND ORGANIZATIONS

The American Dictionary of the English Language, Noah Webster. Facsimile 1828 edition. San Francisco: Foundation for American Christian Education, 1967.

The Bible and the Constitution of the United States of America. Verna M. Hall and Rosalie J. Slater. San Francisco: Foundation for American Christian Education, 1983.

Carry On, Mr. Bowditch Teacher Guide, "American Men of Science and Invention," Rosalie J. Slater. San Francisco: Foundation for American Christian Education, 1970, 4th edition, Rosemarie Ricciardi, ed., 2005.

The Christian History of the American Revolution: Consider and Ponder, 1975; *George Washington, The Character and Influence of One Man,* 2000. Compiled by Verna M. Hall. San Francisco: Foundation for American Christian Education.

The Christian History of the Constitution of the United States of America, Vol. I: *Christian Self-Government,* 1960, and Vol. II: *Christian Self-Government with Union,* 1962. Compiled by Verna M. Hall. San Francisco: Foundation for American Christian Education.

Teaching and Learning America's Christian History: The Principle Approach, by Rosalie J. Slater. San Francisco: Foundation for American Christian Education, 1965.

The Journal of the Foundation for American Christian Education. San Francisco: Foundation for American Christian Education, See especially Vol. V, 1993: "Surveying: A Practical Application of Mathematics in the Life of George Washington" by Maxwell Lyons. "The Electrical Researches of Benjamin Franklin and Nikola Tessla; Model Lessons" by Walter Dimmick.

A Guide to Christian Education for the Home and School: The Principle Approach®. James B. Rose. Palo Cedro, CA: American Christian History Institute, 1987. See "Arithmetic from the Principle Approach," by James V. Kilkenny, and "Algebra from the Principle Approach" by Darold Booton.

Rudiments of America's Christian History and Government: Student Handbook. 1968, 2nd ed., 1984. Rosalie J. Slater and Verna M. Hall. San Francisco: Foundation for American Christian Education.

Foundation for American Christian Education: The Principle Approach, and *The Noah Plan®,* Training seminars in the Principle Approach for homeschool and classroom teachers: I. Foundations, II. Applications. 800-352-3223. www.face.net.

StoneBridge School, Biblical, Historic, Tutorial Education. Foundation for American Christian Education national demonstration school. PO Box 9247, Chesapeake, VA 23321. 757-488-2214, www.stonebridgeschool.com

Bible Math Labs

Dedicated to Mary Lou, Cobus, Kirsten, and Christopher

About the Author:

John Block taught Math and administered in public and private schools from 1978 to 1994. John's wide range of experience (from sixth graders to adult students) and his varied journeys into the world outside the schools, has helped him write interesting and practical curriculum. He also publishes *Math Labs Newsletter.* John is a homeschooling parent as well, with two sons, 9 & 3, and a daughter, 6. John lives and works on a ranch with his wife and children. He also teaches Bible and helps administer at a Christian school.

To order complete book, contact John Block,

Bible Math Labs, HC 79 Box 46, Gothenburg, NE 69138

Of Fish and Fractions

In Matthew 14:15-21, Jesus broke five loaves of bread and two fish into a meal for at least 5,000 men. We know that God multiplied the loaves and fish in order to satisfy the men and leave 12 basketfuls of left over pieces (Matt. 14:20). How much of a loaf and what fraction of a fish would each man have received if Jesus had not trusted God to intervene?

$\frac{\text{5 loaves}}{\text{5000 men}}$ = 1/1000 loaf per man

$\frac{\text{2 fish}}{\text{5000 men}}$ = 1/2500 fish per man

Let's see what a 1/100th of a loaf of bread might look like.

Instructions:

1. Get a whole loaf of pre-sliced bread.
2. Count the number of slices and record on the chart.
3. Cut each piece down the center.

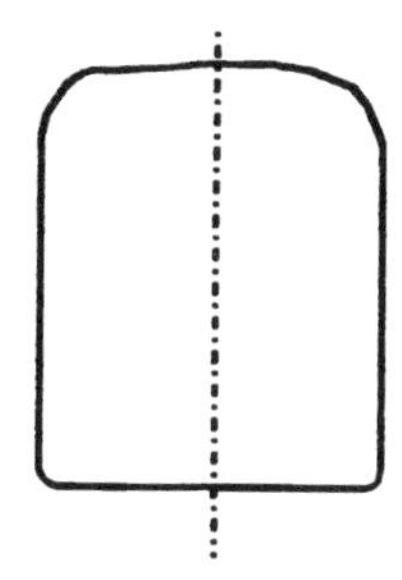

4. Record the number of pieces and fraction of a loaf.
5. Repeat the process until you next fraction will be smaller than 1/1000. **This is about the size 1/1000th of the loaf.**

Cut	Pieces	fraction of loaf
0	20	1/20
1	40	1/40

...and so on.

Cut	# of pieces	Fraction each piece is of loaf

Questions:

•Do you think such small pieces would satisfy your hunger?

•How would the original amount of food compare with the 12 baskets full of leftovers?

•How can you explain satisfied appetites and all the left over pieces?

Of Fish and Fractions, Part 2

Notice how you used fractions to investigate the story of the five loaves and two fish. We could have also use decimals.

Fractions can be written as decimals, because fractions indicate a division problem. For example

$\frac{5}{5000}$ or $5/5000 = 5 \div 5000$

You might say, "But that's two different problems!"

$5/5000 = 1/1000$

and $5 \div 5000 = 5000\overline{)5.000} = .001$

It's really the same problem, or in math terms, $.001 = 1/1000$

.001 is called the <u>decimal equivalent</u> of 1/1000

Every fraction has a <u>decimal equivalent</u>. You can find the decimal equivalent of any fraction by dividing the numerator by the denominator.

$\frac{\text{Numerator}}{\text{Denominator}} = \text{Denominator}\overline{)\text{Numerator}}$

$\frac{1}{2} = 2\overline{)1} = .5$

$\frac{1}{3} = 3\overline{)1} = .\overline{3}...$

(The line over the 3 means that $3\overline{)1}$ gives the answer of 3 over and over, forever.)

$\frac{1}{4} = 4\overline{)1} = .25$

$\frac{1}{5} = 5\overline{)1} = .1\overline{6}...$

Only the 6 repeats forever.

Notice that some of the denominators, (2, 4 and 5 and others) divide evenly into the numerators. They form <u>terminating</u>

numerators. They form <u>terminating</u>
decimals. Other fractions (1/3, 1/6 and others) have decimal patterns which repeat because the denominators do not divide evenly into the numerators.. These decimals are called <u>repeating</u>.

Let's review.

- A fraction is also a division problem.
- Each fraction has a <u>decimal equivalent.</u>
- A decimal equivalent is found by dividing:

denominator $\overline{)\text{numerator}}$

- Decimal equivalents are either <u>terminating</u> or <u>repeating</u>.

Instructions:

1. Use your calculator (or long division) to fill out the fish and Fractions Data Sheet.
2. Indicate the number of places that terminate and/or repeat.

1/4 = .25 2T
1.3 = $.\overline{3}$... 1R
1/6 = $.1\overline{6}$... 1T 1R
etc.

3. Recognize patterns and describe under the "Conclusions" column.
4. Find decimal equivalents through denominator of 20. Many fractions will reduce to lower denominators:

3/6 = 1/2, 4/12 = 1/3 etc.

When a fraction reduces, go on to the next fraction.

Changing fractions to decimals may seem like a boring task, but a wealth of patterns exists in the decimal equivalents.

Every decimal either terminates or repeats. Some decimal equivalents seem to terminate and repeat! There are also many interesting patterns. Here are some examples.

1/5 = .2
2/5 = .4
3/5 = .6 — 1T (terminates with 1 place)
4/5 = .8 — What interesting pattern do you see?

1/8 = .125
3/8 = .375
5/8 = .625 — 3T (terminates with 3 places)
7/8 = .875 — Another interesting pattern?

1/3 = $.\overline{3}$...
2/3 = $.\overline{6}$... — 1R (repeats with 1 place)

1/7 = $\overline{.142857}$... — 6R (repeats 6 places)
2/7 = $\overline{.285714}$... — Also notice that the same
3/7 = $\overline{.428571}$... — six numbers repeat with
4/7 = $\overline{.571428}$... — a different 1st digit.

1/12 = $.08\overline{3}$... — Each is 2T 1R. Is 1/12 a
5/12 = $.41\overline{6}$... — combo if 1/4 and 1/3?
7/12 = $.58\overline{3}$... — Same repeaters as 1/3!

The data gathered in this lab will be used in the following lab, *Picture That ...A Fraction.*

Questions:

1. How do you convert a fraction to its decimal equivalent?
2. What do the terms "repeating" and "terminating" mean?
3. What interesting patterns did you find in the decimal equivalents?
4. Kid you find similarities of decimals of fractions with the same denominator?
5. If a denominator can be factored (the 8 of 1/8 can be written as 2 x4), are there similarities between the decimals whose denominators are the factors? For instance, compare the decimal patterns of 1/8, 1/4, and 1/2. Or compare 1/6, 1/3, and 1/2.

Fish and Fractions Data Sheet

Fraction	Reduced	Dec. Equiv.	Repeat./Term. Pat.	Conclusions

Picture That...a Fraction

In our last lab, Of Fish and Fractions, you hopefully found some interesting patterns in the decimal equivalents of fractions. You can make those patterns even more apparent by drawing them! I'll give you a few different ways to draw pictures of fractions, and then you can take it from there and devise some of your own ways.

Our first picture method is called, URDL...

1. On a sheet of graph paper, mark a starting point where two grid lines intersect.
2. Draw a dark line up, as many squares as the tenths digit.
3. From the top of that line, draw a dark line to the right, as many squares as the hundredths digit. Down as many as the thousandths digits. Left, and the up again and so forth until there are no digits remaining.

Look at the examples below.

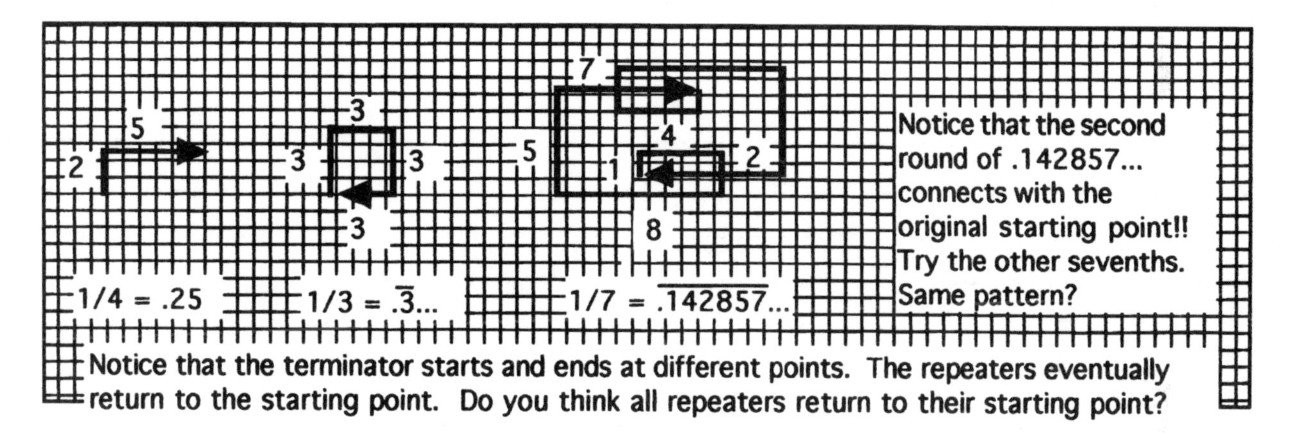

Instead of the URDL... pattern above, use a slightly different pattern, such as URUR...or URUL...I call the RURD...the Wandering Pattern. Try 1/7 with RURD... Do repeaters still make distinctive patterns?

Here's another pattern, which I call the Plant pattern or Arrow Feather pattern. Each digit in the decimal equivalent is an alternating left or right flag on a stem or arrow.

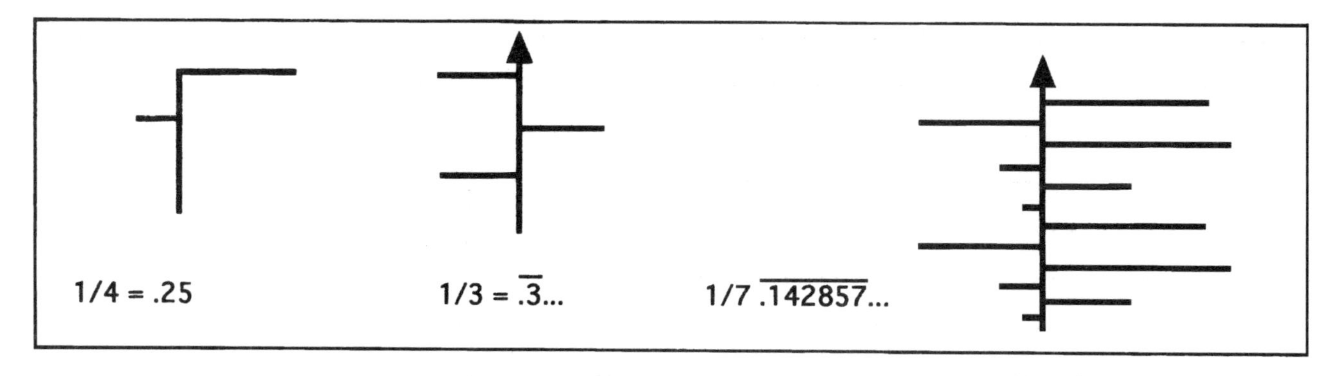

Make up some of your own systems for picturing a fraction.

Picture That...A Fraction

Basic Geometric Shapes

Look around you and then answer this question, "What shape are most of the objects around you?" Where I am sitting, I see books, boxes, cupboards, and book shelves, which all have the same basic shape. Even my desk has that shape.

What is the most common shape? If you said, "Box, square, or rectangle," you are probably close enough. Actually, all these shapes--books, boxes, cupboards, etc.--are **rectangular prisms**.

Rectangular prisms are probably the most common geometric shapes. The faces are rectangles, are parallel to the opposite face, and meet at right angles.

Here's an easy way to draw rectangular prisms and other geometric shapes.

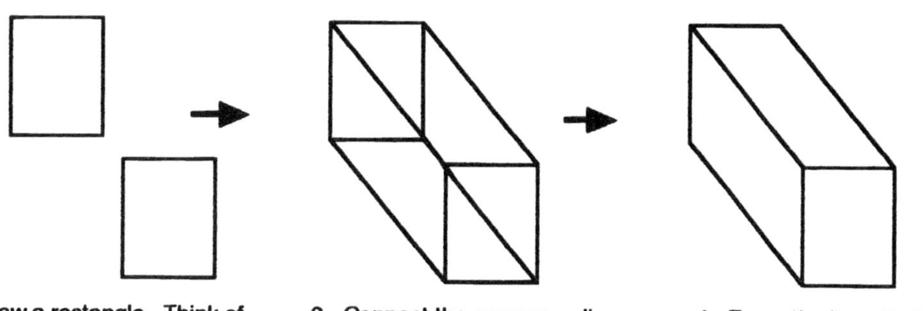

1. Draw a rectangle. Think of it as lying on the plane of the paper.
2. Draw an identical rectangle as if it is lying somewhere behind.

3. Connect the corresponding corners with straight lines.

4. Erase the lines that would be hidden.

Triangular Prism (triangle used as base)

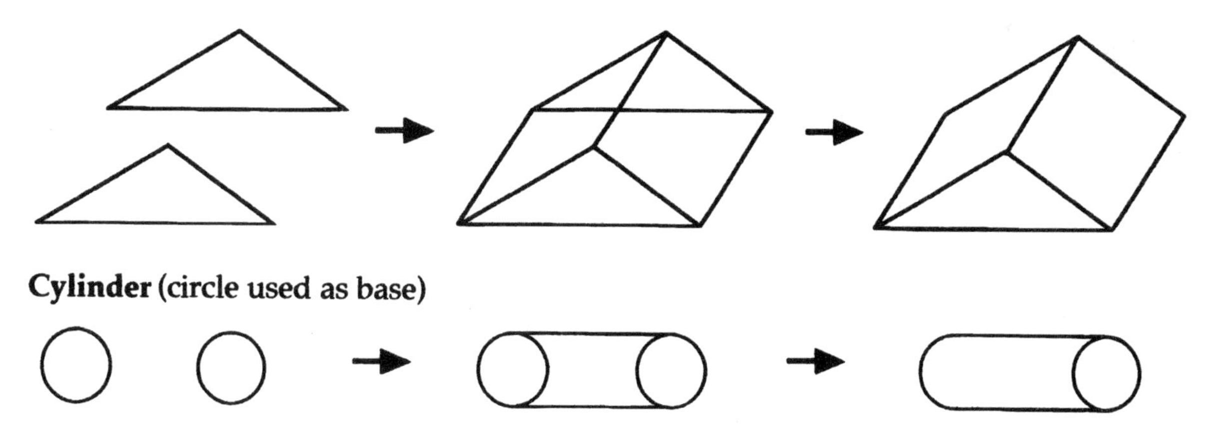

Cylinder (circle used as base)

Does the cylinder look "not quite right?" A cone drawn with this method will look even more unnatural (fig. 1). Why? Because it is not drawn in perspective. It is impossible to see the full circle and the full side of the cone at the same time. The base of the cone should appear like an oval (fig. 2).

Rectangular prisms and other geometric shapes can also be drawn with perspective. Use the technique as above, but draw the bases or front and back faces as if you are seeing them at an angle.

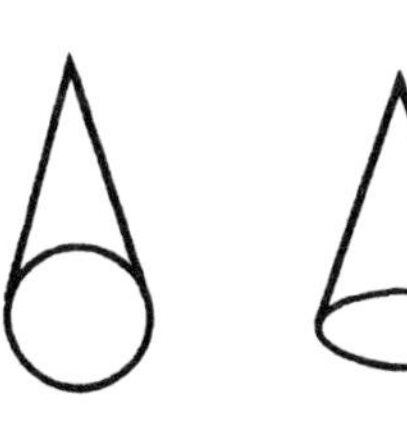

fig. 1 fig. 2

Rectangular Prism

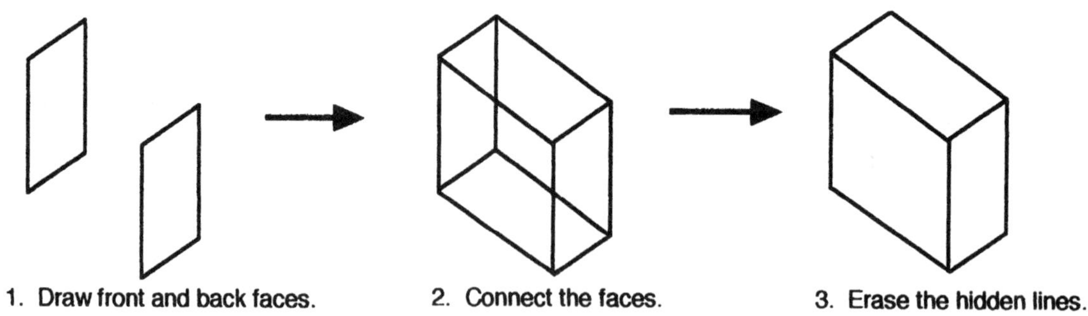

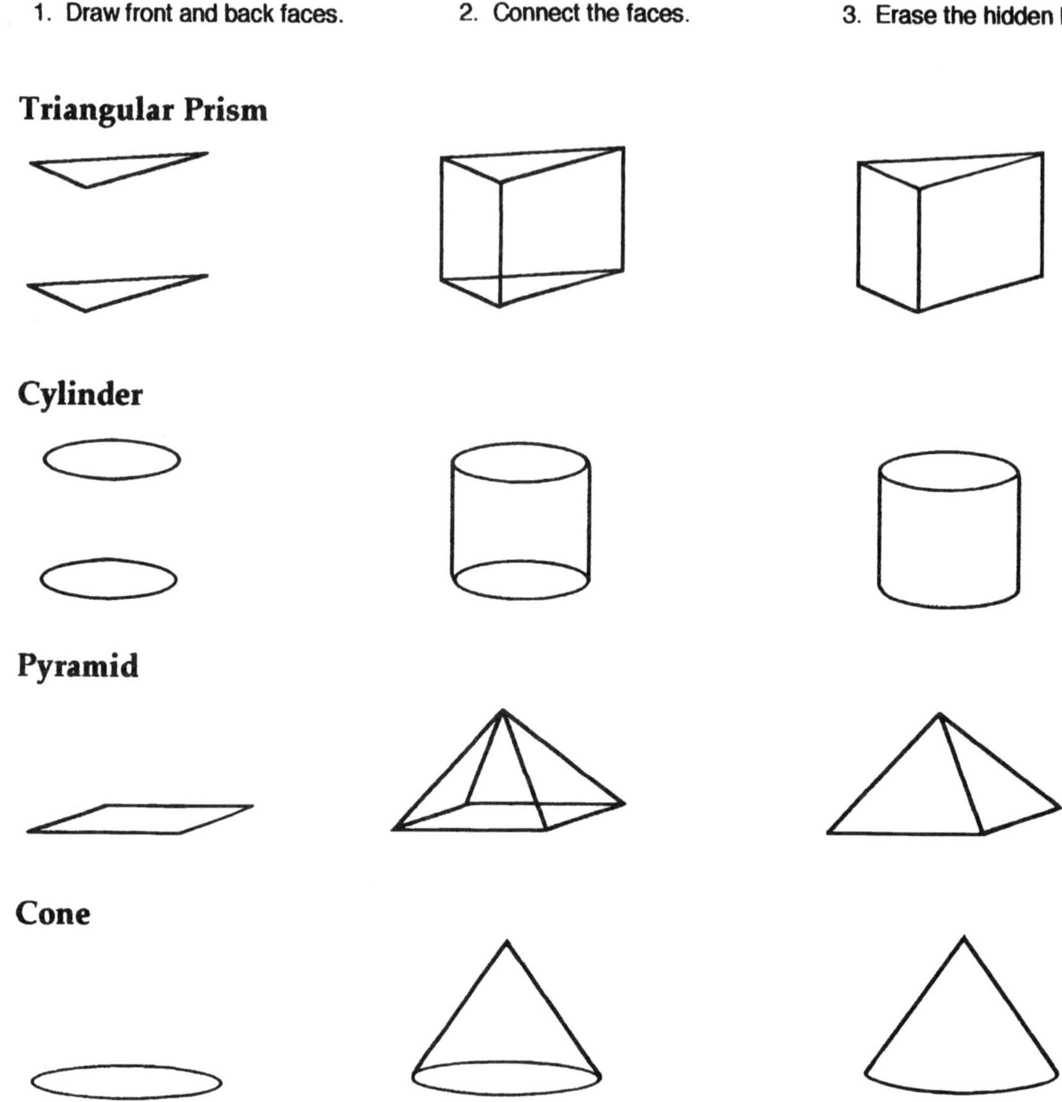

Your Turn

•Practice drawing each of the geometric shapes. Experiment, try different angles and sizes. Place the back face in different places with regard to the front face.
•Try combining shapes to form composite shapes, for instance, put a pramid on top of a rectangular prism, something like the Washington Monument.

Applying The Shapes

In *Geometric Shapes,* we drew a rectangular prism in a way that placed one face in the plane of the paper, and another face in a plane behind the paper (parallel to the paper).

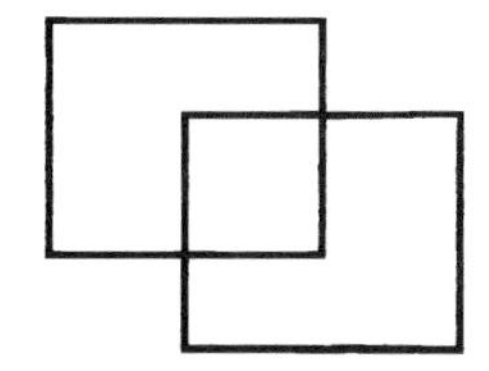

Connecting these two faces, we have a rectangular prism.

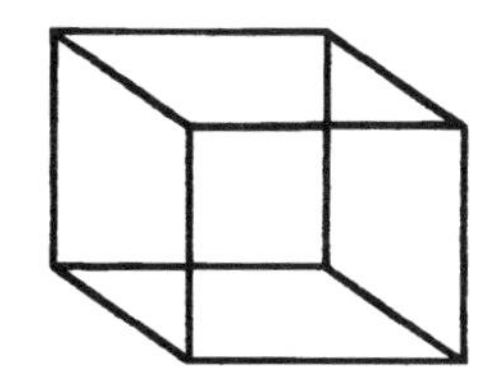

The edges of the rectangular prism lie in three different directions.

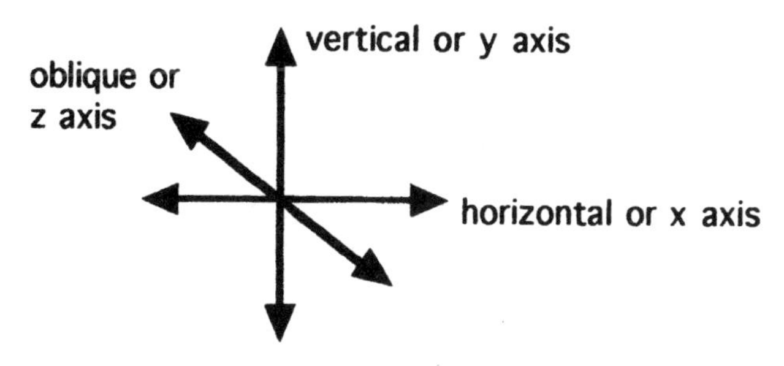

Imagine the horizontal and vertical axes on the paper, and the oblique axis going back into the paper.

Let's use the rectangular prism and the x, y, and z axes to draw a simple building.

All horizontal lines in the building will be in either the x or z direction. All vertical lines will be in the y direction.

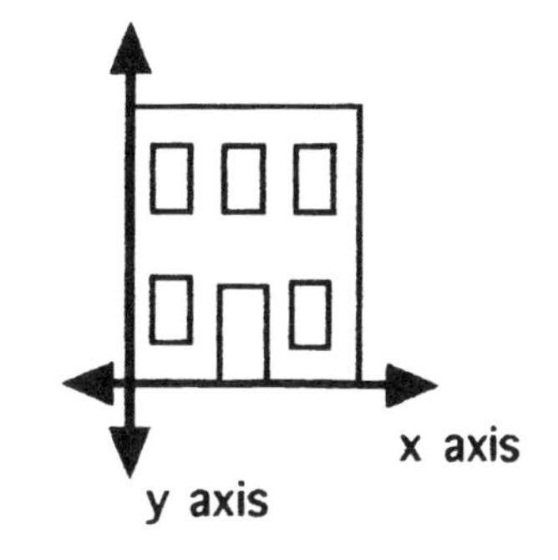

The doors and windows on the front face align with the x & y axes.

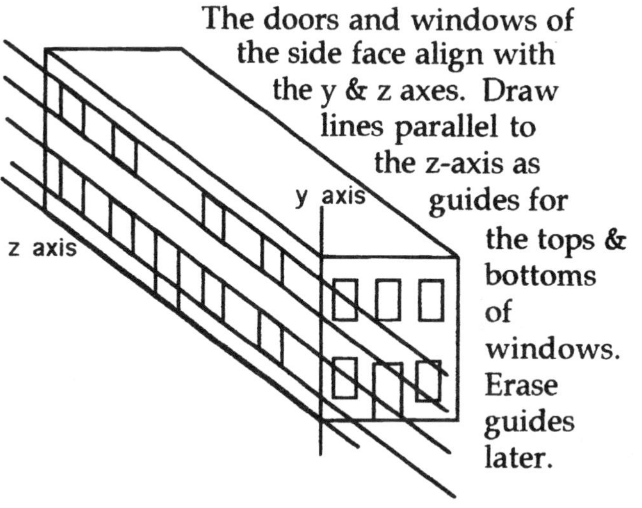

The doors and windows of the side face align with the y & z axes. Draw lines parallel to the z-axis as guides for the tops & bottoms of windows. Erase guides later.

We know that the windows and doors on the side are rectangles, but what happened to the right angles?

Hold a book in front of you, then turn it at different angles. Does the cover always look like a rectangle with square corners?

Look at buildings in your neighborhood or town. Do you see how you could draw them with the help of the x, y, and z axes? When doesn't this system work very well?

1. Draw a rectangular building that you've seen in your neighborhood or town. Use the x, y, and z axes to set up the drawing and to check the alignment of the doors and windows.
2. Draw other objects in your house that have basic geometric shapes. Use the x, y, and z axes.

Applying The Shapes, Part 2

Imagine turning the top of the y axis so that the x axis is oblique (going back into the page) like the z axis.

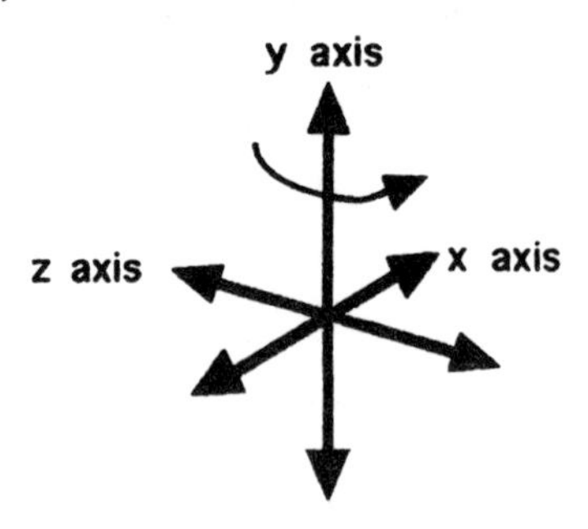

The building will look slightly different with the axes turned.

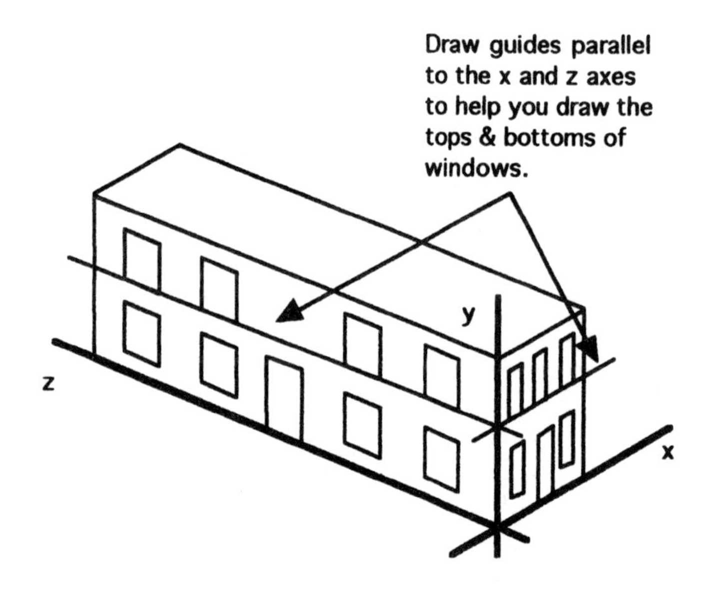

Notice that the lines through the tops and bottoms of the windows and doors are parallel to the z axis or x axis. The vertical sides of the windows and doors are parallel to the y axis. This is helpful when drawing.

Remember These Drawing Hints:

- All vertical lines are parallel to the y axis.
- All horizontal lines are parallel to the x axis or the z axis, depending on what plane they are parallel to.

Instructions:

Redraw the buildings you drew for the last page with the new set of axes.

In the drawing at the right, notice the base line of the building along the z axis and the vertical corner line which we can't see. Do they intersect? Are they then parallel?

Further Exploration: To explore perspective drawing further see
How To Use Creative Perspective by Ernest W. Watson, Reinhold Publishing Co.
Perspective by Alison Cole, Dorling Kindersley, Inc.

Composite Shapes

Objects made up of two or more simple shapes are called composites. For instance, consider the following description:

> A rectangular prism about 4' high, with a smaller rectangular prism (same width and depth) stacked on top of it. Two thin rectangular prisms fitted on the front of the first rectangular prisms.

At first, this is confusing, but when we erase the hidden lines, and add a couple of long, then rectangular handles, we can easily see...

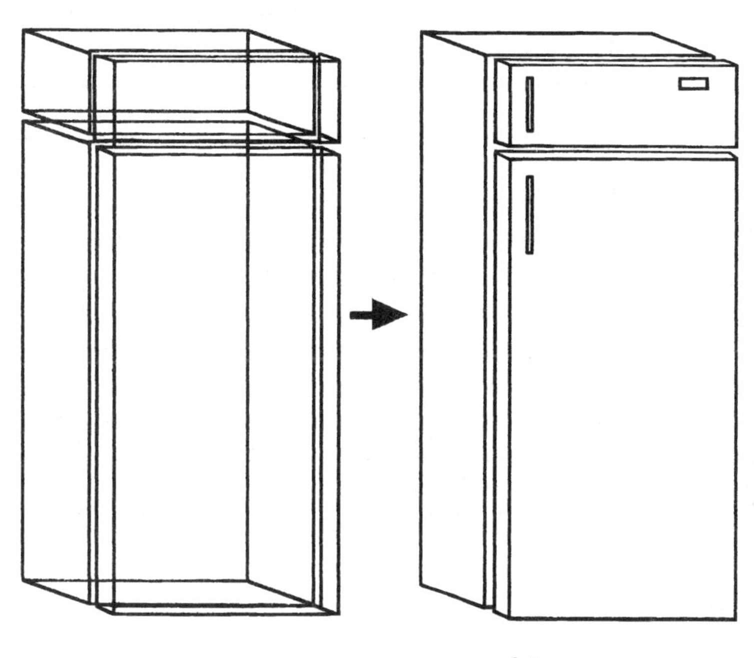

... a refrigerator.

Many things we see and use every day have composite shapes. Consider a house. No matter how simple or fancy, a house breaks down into several basic geometric shapes. Look at the house below.

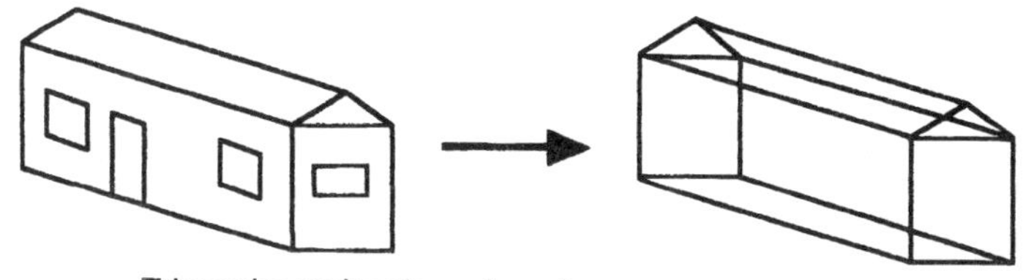

Triangular and rectangular prisms.

How many rectangular prisms can you find in the house below? How many triangular prisms?

Below, two cones combine to make a funnel.

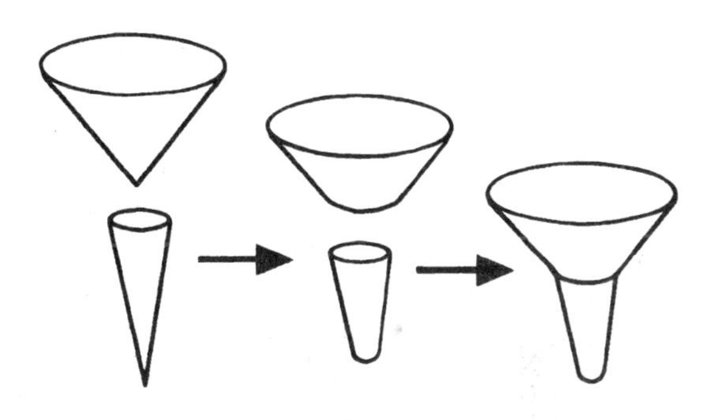

Instructions

1. List the simple geometric shapes that make up the following: dad's shaving cream can, mom's mixer, electric drill, pop bottle.
2. Look at other things in your house or apartment. What simple geometric shapes compose them? Record in the chart on the next page.
3. Observe the houses on your street or in a nearby neighborhood. Determine and record the geometric shapes they are composed of.
4. Draw a composite figure. Label the shapes composing it.

Write the names of objects in your house or apartment, yard or neighborhood in the first column. Analyze the objects and record the geometric shapes they are composed of in the second and third columns.

Object	2-Dimensional Shapes	3-Dimensional Shapes

Sample Student Notebook Pages

An American Christian Approach
to the Study of
Arithmetic

Taught by: Mrs. Ricciardi

Prepared by: Ricky S.

September 11, 2000

Arithmetic

I. The word "arithmetic" comes from the Greek word "arithmeo" meaning "to number."

II Arithmetic is the science of numbers or the Art of computation.

A. "Science" means knowledge.
B. "Art" means skill.
C. "Computation" means numbering.
*D. Arithmetic is the knowledge of numbers and the use of numbers.

September 11, 2000

Origin of Arithmetic

1 Father
2 Son
3 Holy Spirit

I. God's nature is the origin of Arithmetic.
  A. God always has existed.
  B. The idea of number 1 started with God because He always was the first thing - John 1:3.

II. God is made up of the Trinity consisting of God the Father, God the Son, and God the Holy Spirit - I John 5:7

Ricky September 12, 2000

Purpose of Arithmetic

I. The purpose of arithmetic is:
  1. to know God through the Bible and learn of his character
  2. to make God known to other people, and
  3. to have dominion (control) over the earth.
    a. Taking dominion is to take charge of our situations as spending your money.

September 13, 2000

God's Character in Numbers.

I. Many of God's character traits can be seen in numbers.
A. God is orderly. Numbers have order - Genesis 1:31.
B. God is never-ending. Numbers go on forever - Hebrews 13:18.
C. God is unchanging. Numbers are unchangeable - James 1:17.

Ricky September 13, 2000

Arithmetic and the History of Liberty

I. Asia is the continent where our number system began.
A. The Hindu people in India invented the number system (1, 2, 3,).

II. Euorope is the continent where Arithmetic developed.
A. The Hindu system was adopted by the Arabs, who spread it across the Mediterranean region.
B. The invention of the printing press also helped to spread the Hindu Arabic System throughout.

III. America is the continent where Arithmetic has helped bring liberty for the individual.

September 13, 2000

A. The Pilgrims brought the printing press to America.

B. Our government allowed Arithmetic to grow.

September 18, 2000

Sums With Even Numbers

8=

8=6+2 | 8=4+2+2
8=4+4 | 8=2+2+2+2

12=

12=10+2 | 12=6+2+2+2
12=8+4 | 12=4+4+4
12=8+2+2 | 12=4+4+2+2
12=6+6 | 12=4+2+2+2+2
12=6+4+2 | 12=2+2+2+2+2+2

Ricky September 18, 2000

10 =

10 = 8 + 2 10 = 4 + 2 + 2 + 2
10 = 6 + 4 10 = 2 + 2 + 6
10 = 6 + 2 + 2 10 = 2 + 2 + 2 + 2 + 2

September 29, 2000

Multiples of 2 and 4

2 (4) 6 (8) 10
(12) 14 (16) 18 (20)
22 (24) 26 (28) 30
(32) 34 (36) 38 (40)

4 8 12 16 20
24 28 32 36 40

November 13, 2000

Multiples of "5"

5 10 55 55×6=330
15 20 55
25 30 55 55 multiplicand
35 40 55 ×6 multiplier
45 50 55 product
+55
330

Worksheet 15, Musical Notes

Name Richard

Date 10-24-00

1. Write the notes and their names in the chart below. Also write the number of beats.

Beats	Notes	Name
4	whole note	whole
2	two half notes	half
1	four quarter notes	quarter
½	eight eighth notes	eighth

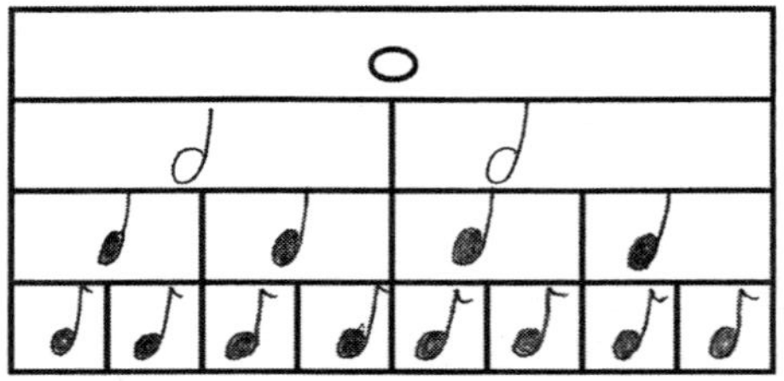

2. Draw notes to complete the measures. Draw a note on each line.

4/4

4/4

4/4

4/4

3: © Joan A. Cotter 1999

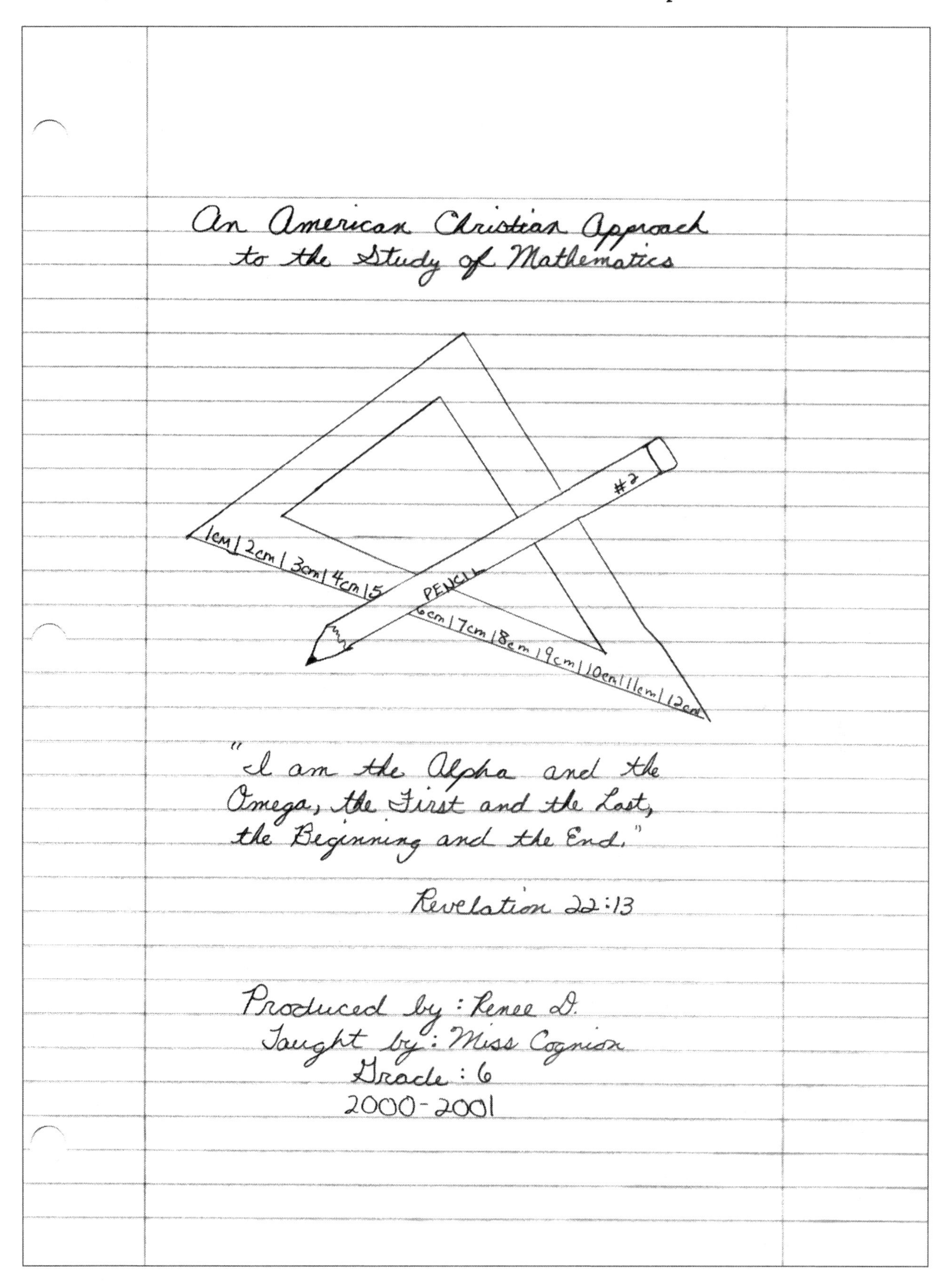
An American Christian Approach
to the Study of Mathematics
1cm | 2cm | 3cm | 4cm | 5
6cm | 7cm | 8cm | 9cm | 10cm | 11cm | 12cm
PENCIL
#2
"I am the Alpha and the
Omega, the First and the Last,
the Beginning and the End."
Revelation 22:13
Produced by: Renee D.
Taught by: Miss Cognion
Grade: 6
2000-2001

Miss Cognion — Renee D.

Arithmetic — September 11, 2000

Biblical Source or Origin of Mathematics

Genesis 1:1

"In the beginning God created the heavens and the earth."

In the first three words of Genesis 1:1 I learned that there is a beginning, there will be an end and observed the word measurement. We measure the beginning to the end. ✓

the beginning (earth) —————— the end (fire)

Revelation 1:8

"'I am the Alpha and the Omega,' says the Lord God, 'who is, and who was, and who is to come, the Almighty.'"

Math — Renee D.

Miss Cognion — September 13, 2000

Numeration & Notation

Numeration is the method of reading numbers.

Notation is the method of writing numbers.

0 also called zero, naught, or cipher.

11 - derived from Saxon and means "one left after ten".

12 - "two left after ten"

Table of Orders

619, 853, 462, 843, 560, 178

Digit	Order	Name
6	8th	hundred quad
1	7th	ten quad
9	6th	quadrillion
8	15th	hundred trill
5	14th	ten trill
3	13th	trillion
4	12th	hundred bill
6	11th	ten bill
2	10th	billion
8	9th	hundred mill
4	8th	ten mill
3	7th	million
5	6th	hundred thou
6	5th	ten thou
0	4th	thousands
1	3rd	hundreds
7	2nd	tens
8	1st	ones or unit

Miss Cognion   Renee D.
Arithmetic   September 19, 2000

Addition

Addition is the process of uniting 2 or more like numbers into 1 equivalent number.

```
   234 ← addend
 4,095 ← addend
+   75 ← addend
 4,404 ← sum
```

Principles

1. Only like numbers can be added.
2. The sum is equal to all the units of all the parts.
3. The sum is the same in kind as the numbers added.
4. Units of the same order, and only such, can be added directly.
5. The sum is the same in whatever succession the numbers are added.

Miss Cognion   Renee D.
Arithmetic   September 20, 2000

Subtraction

Subtraction is the process of finding the difference between 2 numbers of the same kind.

```
  129 ← minuend . . . "to be diminished"
- 36 ← subtrahend . . "to be subtracted"
  93 ← difference
```

Miss Cognion — Renee D.
Arithmetic — September 22, 2000
p. 31

Multiplication

<u>Multiplication</u> is taking one number as many times (×) as there are units (ones) in another;

* 2. <u>Multiplication</u> is a short method of adding numbers that are equal.

```
 ⁴178 ← Multiplicand
×   6 ← Multiplier
1,068 ← Product
```

Concrete: 182 hot dogs   41 hours of t.v.
          96 frogs   39 potatoes

vs.

Abstract: 182   41
          96   39

Miss Cognion — Renee D.
Arithmetic — September 26, 2000

Division

<u>Division</u> is the process of finding how many times one number is contained in another; or

2. <u>Division</u> is a short method of making several subtractions of the same number.

```
 ¹24¹⁴
 - 7   1x
  17
 - 7   2x
  10
 - 7   3x
   3
```

```
                  (quoties)
          3      quotient - Latin "how often"
divisor 7)24     dividend - "to be divided"
         -21
           3     remainder
```

Miss Cognion Renee D.
Arithmetic September 28, 2000

The Five-Step Method

1. Problem: copy down the problem.

2. Given: finding the key elements
... What information is provided?

3. Find: What do I need to find?

4. Analysis: The "how to" step - How to solve the problem.

5. Solution: Solving the problem.

Miss Cognion Renee D.
Math p.56 October 3, 2000

The Five-Step Method

1. Problem: A farmer bought 25 acres of land for $2,675: what did 19 acres of it cost?

Given: 25 acres cost $2,675.

Find: · the value of each acre.
· the value of 19 acres. Use sentences.

Analysis: · divide $2,675 by 25
· multiply the value of each acre by 19.

Solution:

· 25) 2,675 = $107

· 107 x 19 = 963 + 1070 = $2,033 for 19 acres

Be concrete!

Miss Cognion   Renee D.
Arithmetic   October 3, 2000

Properties of Numbers

The properties of numbers are those qualities which belong to them.

Numbers are classified as:

1. Integral, fractional, and mixed

Integer = whole # — 21, 49, 6

1/2, 3/4, 9/10

6 3/4

2. Abstract and Concrete

100,417 — 100,417 cats

3. Prime and Composite

Divisible by 1 & itself

Prime	Composite
2 (1,2)	8(1,2,4,8)
5 (1,5)	6(1,2,3,6)
3 (1,3)	4 (1,2,4)
11(1,11)	

Miss Cognion   Renee D.
Math   October 19, 2000

The Greatest Common Divisor

Case I: By simple factoring

(5) 85 120
 17 24

G.C.D. of 85 and 120 is (5).

Case II: By successive division

85) 120 (1
 −85
 35) 85 (2
 −70
 15) 35 (2
 −30
 (5)) 15 (3
 −15
 0

Miss Cognion
Math p.76

Renee D.
November 7, 2000

Fractions

A fraction may be considered as an indicated division in which,

1. The dividend is the numerator.
2. The divisor is the denominator.
3. The quotient is the fraction itself.

$\frac{4}{12}$ } 12⟌4

quotient

Common fractions are divided into two classes:

1. As to value, Proper and Improper.
   - Proper - one whose numerator is smaller than the denominator.
     $\frac{6}{18}$, $\frac{4}{12}$, $\frac{3}{9}$, $\frac{1}{14}$, $\frac{2}{4}$, $\frac{3}{6}$, $\frac{119,216}{345,020}$
   - Improper - one whose numerator is larger than the denominator.
     $\frac{2}{1}$, $\frac{6}{3}$, $\frac{1,020}{3}$, $\frac{3}{2}$, $\frac{100}{50}$, $\frac{178,000}{2}$

Miss Cognion
Math

Renee D.
November 7, 2000

Fractions

2. As to form, Simple, Compound, or Complex
   - Simple - a single fraction whose terms are integral
     $\frac{3}{4}$, $\frac{9}{2}$, $\frac{10}{34}$, $\frac{22}{7}$ (whole #)
   - Compound - a fraction of a fraction $\frac{3}{4} \times \frac{7}{8} = \frac{17}{9} \times \frac{9}{74}$ (x)
   - Complex - one which has one or both of its terms fractional.
     $\frac{5\frac{1}{2}}{7}$ $\frac{5}{7\frac{1}{2}}$ $\frac{5\frac{1}{2}}{7\frac{1}{2}}$

Miss Cognion — Renee D.
Math — November 7, 2000

Reduction of Fractions

Reduction of fractions consists of changing their form and not their value.

Case I: Reduction of fractions to their lowest terms. (N & D)

Rule: Divide both terms of the fraction by their G.C.D.

Examples: Reduce $\frac{30}{45}$ to its lowest term.

$$5 \overline{)30 \quad 45} \qquad 3 \overline{)6 \quad 9} \qquad 2 \quad 3 \qquad G.C.D. = 15$$

$$30 \div 15 = 2, \quad 45 \div 15 = 3 \quad \to \frac{2}{3}$$

$$3 \overline{)12 \quad 48} \qquad 2 \overline{)4 \quad 16} \qquad 2 \overline{)2 \quad 8} \qquad 1 \quad 4 = \frac{1}{4}$$

$$2 \overline{)14 \quad 36} \qquad 7 \quad 18 \qquad \frac{14}{36} = \frac{1}{18}$$

Miss Cognion — Renee D.
Math p. 79 — November 10, 2000

Fractions

Case II: Reduction of fractions to their higher terms.

Rule: 1. Divide the required denominator by the denominator of the given fraction.
2. Multiply both terms of the given fraction by this quotient.
3. The result is the equivalent fraction required.

Example: $\frac{1 \times 12}{3 \times 12} = \frac{12}{36} \qquad \frac{4 \times 7}{5 \times 7} = \frac{28}{35} \qquad \frac{2 \times 10}{3 \times 10} = \frac{20}{30}$

Miss Cognion — Renee D.
Math p. 80 — November 27, 2000

Fractions
Case III

Case III – To reduce (change form not value) a whole or mixed number to an improper fraction.

Rule: 1. Multiply together the whole number and the denominator of the fraction.

2. To the product add the numerator, and

3. Write the sum over the denominator.

Examples: $3\frac{1}{5} = \frac{16}{5}$ $6\frac{2}{7} = \frac{44}{7}$

$7\frac{4}{8} = \frac{60}{8}$ $10\frac{5}{6} = \frac{65}{6}$

$36\frac{2}{3} = \frac{110}{3}$

Miss Cognion — Renee D.
Math — November 28, 2000

Fractions:
Case III

Case III: Reduction of whole or mixed numbers to improper fractions.

1. $5\frac{1}{4} = \frac{21}{4}$
2. $7\frac{2}{3} = \frac{23}{3}$
3. $5\frac{6}{9} = \frac{51}{9}$
4. $10\frac{8}{10} = \frac{108}{10}$
5. $9\frac{4}{6} = \frac{58}{6}$
6. $22\frac{4}{5} = \frac{114}{5}$
7. $12\frac{9}{10} = \frac{131}{10} = \frac{129}{10}$
8. $6\frac{5}{8} = \frac{53}{8}$
9. $11\frac{7}{8} = \frac{95}{8}$
10. $4\frac{3}{7} = \frac{31}{7}$
11. $3\frac{8}{10} = \frac{38}{10}$
12. $7\frac{7}{9} = \frac{70}{9}$
13. $4\frac{5}{6} = \frac{29}{6}$
14. $1\frac{3}{4} = \frac{7}{4}$
15. $100\frac{4}{5} = \frac{504}{5}$

Bonus:

$121\frac{13}{15} = \frac{1,828}{15}$

Arithmetic
p 25 #18

Brittany
9/13/02

5-Step Review

1st Given: Man bought 3 bales of cotton
1st $325 - cost
2nd $16 more than 1st bale
3rd as much as both of the others

2 Find: What is the total cost for all 3 bales?

3 Analysis:
1. Add the cost of the first bale + 16 to find the cost of bale 2
2. Find the cost of the third bale by adding the cost of bale 1 to bale 2.
3. Add the cost of bale 1, bale 2, and bale 3 for total cost.

4 Solution:

1. $325 + $16 = $341 (2nd bale)

2. $325 + $341 = 666 (3rd bale)

3. $666 + $341 + $325 = $1,332 (total cost)

5 Check:

1. $341 ✓ − $16 = 325

2. $666 ✓ − $341 = 325

3. $341 + $666 + $325 = 1,332

Algebra
Mrs. Hunnewell

Jordan L.
October 11, 2004

Using Identity and Equality Properties

I Peter 3:15 "...Always be prepared to give an answer to everyone who asks you to give the reason for the hope that you have."

Evaluate each expression, giving the reason or property which governs each step:

1. $2\left[\frac{1}{4}+\left(\frac{1}{2}\right)^2\right]$

$= 2\left(\frac{1}{4}+\frac{1}{4}\right)$ Substitution

$= 2\left(\frac{1}{2}\right)$ Substitution

$= 1$ Multiplicative Inverse

2. $15 \cdot 1 - 9 + 2(15 \div 3 - 5)$

$= 15 \cdot 1 - 9 + 2(5-5)$ Substitution

$= 15 \cdot 1 - 9 + 2(0)$ Substitution

$= 15 \cdot 1 - 9 + 0$ Mult. Prop. of Zero

$= 15 - 9 + 0$ Mult. Identity

$= 6 - 0$ Substitution

$= 6$ Substitution